EVEN BETTER
after 50

HOW TO BECOME (AND REMAIN)
WELL OF BODY, **WISE** OF MIND,
AND **WHOLE** OF SPIRIT
IN THE SECOND HALF OF YOUR LIFE

RICHARD P. JOHNSON, PH.D.

ISBN 978-0-9743623-6-6

10 9 8 7 6 5 4 3 2 1

First Edition

Cover design by Megan Irwin

Printed in the United States of America

Preface

This book gives a panoramic yet practical overview of how to live optimally ... how to be your best ... how to live fully in your 50s, 60s, 70s, 80s, and beyond!

The exciting ideas in this book first took root in my work as the Director of Behavioral Sciences in a large teaching medical center where for 15 years I taught hundreds of medical doctors the "Art of Medicine." There I learned that ...

Optimal health is a mixture of many factors – all acting in harmony.

This book describes the <u>12 fundamental competencies</u> (some call them 'secrets') of creating exceptional wellness in the second half of life. It guides you so you can easily learn and adopt these competencies to create your own personal optimal wellness plan.

This book breaks new ground; it is NOT a warmed-over academic analysis of medical research. Rather, it offers fresh ideas, an entirely new perspective, and innovative thinking framed for the first time by a wholesome spiritual dimension of health that illuminates and inspires.

Maturing Adult: Throughout this book I refer to "maturing adults." For our purposes, a "maturing adult" is

Even Better After 50

one who has reached the age of 50. There's really nothing magical about 50 (any more than any other age), it merely serves as a convenient chronological benchmark and entry point into "middle age." While the term "maturing adult" is somewhat vague, I find it less offensive than other terms that are often used to describe the second half of life.

While this book certainly stands on its own, its value can be dramatically enhanced by pairing it with a video educational program by the same title. Please log onto: www.SeniorAdultMinistry.com to learn more.

Contents

Introduction

Wellness is an all-encompassing notion that includes finding fulfillment on three levels of human living:

1. The physical level, which we simply call **well.**
2. The mental health level or wellness of the mind, which we call **wise.**
3. The spiritual level, which we call **whole.**

In every life phase and stage we seek to become and remain well, wise, and whole. This is particularly important in the maturing years, for it is at this stage that we develop a sufficient level of maturation necessary to "get a better grip" on these three aspects of wellness in a comprehensive way. Each of these three levels of human functioning can be seen as requiring special skills or areas of skills that together contribute mightily to a maturing adult's ability to find wellness and well being.

A model for well, wise, and whole living has emerged from my research and clinical observations over the years. This model includes four goals in each of the three health dimensions: 1) four for the well dimension, 2) four for the wise dimension, and 3) four for the whole dimension, for a total of 12 goals. Each of the 12 chapters in the book is exclusively devoted to one of these goals.

BODY-MIND INTERACTION

Wellness is a process rather than a destination. Leading medical practitioners uniformly insist that the interactions of our body functions, our mind, and our innate spirit determine our overall wellness. These authorities are united in their belief that people can exercise power and choice in determining how these factors interact together in their lives.

So often maturing adults are unaware of the many facets of wellness and how a general lack of wellness can hobble their lives. This lack of wellness then prevents them from achieving an overall sense of health and well-being that erodes their sense of personal fulfillment and meaning, and squeezes a sense of happiness out of their lives. These maturing adults lack no intelligence. What they do lack is a comprehensive understanding of how so many factors interact to create overall wellness. For the first time, this book offers comprehensive understanding and practical wellness techniques in one place.

With the information in this book, you can develop new personal insights that will prepare you to look with new eyes upon your own wellness and well-being, and to take the necessary steps so you can become as "well" as you possibly can be!

WELL, WISE, AND WHOLE

What is wellness and well being to you? How do you, or any "maturing" adult, strive to accomplish this goal of wellness? Certainly as we proceed along the maturation path of life, we encounter sickness and illness that can throw us into a lifestyle quite far from what we would want for ourselves. One of the ways that you can help motivate yourself to begin or intensify a comprehensive health improvement program is to undertake a personal assessment of where you are right now in your health promotion beliefs and attitudes. This book gives you this opportunity.

With appreciation,

Richard P. Johnson, Ph.D.

Part One

Achieving Lifelong Wellness

THE *BODY* DIMENSION OF OPTIMAL HEALTH

There are many definitions of wellness, but the one I like best is ...

Wellness is the state of living fully.

Full living means finding maximum fulfillment from all areas of life: occupational, familial, financial, relational, educational, spiritual, and of course, physical.

Wellness is not simply the absence of disease; wellness has clear attitudinal qualities. Health is a very personal thing - a state of thriving, not simply surviving. Wellness means adding life to your years, not simply years to your life.

The four goals for the *well* dimension of health for Maturing adults are...

5

Chapter One: **Building Lifespan Vitality.** Maturing adults who actively pursue this goal like the feeling of knowing that they are doing what is necessary to keep the marvelous machine of their body in top running condition. They feed it correctly, get proper rest, maintain a regular exercise program, and perform other health maintenance and promotion activities that help their bodies perform maximally.

Chapter Two: **Mastering the Psychology of Leisure.** Maturing adults who are "well" develop and maintain a mindset that values and fosters a strong leisure component. These maturing adults generate increased personal power because they regularly enter into activities that give rest and respite for the body, stimulation for the mind, and enrichment for the soul.

Chapter Three: **Taking Charge of Life.** Healthy maturing adults strive to shoulder dependable and responsible actions so that growth and development occur smoothly in the various arenas of their lives. They give conscious attention to their lives so that they smooth the way for continued growth. They develop personal wellness goals and seem to have the "follow through" to see these goals toward success. They don't just make wishes or resolutions, they don't simply hope that wellness will somehow emerge, and they don't presume that they will continue as they always have. On the contrary, they make specific plans and take active steps to position themselves in ways that allow maximum health to come their way.

Chapter Four: **Continuous Health Self-Improvement.** Healthy maturing adults see themselves on a continuous self-improvement program. They regularly strive to make themselves better today than they were yesterday. This improvement can be in any area of their lives: physical, intellectual, financial, leisure, spiritual, etc. Flexibility, malleability, and adaptability are all aspects of the same life issue – change. These maturing adults believe that change is supposed to happen and so they engineer their lives so it will occur in as positive a direction as they can influence. They realize they can't control life, but they can influence it in healthful ways.

Chapter One

Building Lifespan Vitality

Building Lifespan Vitality is the degree to which you practice physical healthcare essentials and value yourself.

Who among us doesn't want to remain well and fit for as long possible? We hear so much about longevity enhancement today, yet aren't we actually more interested in investing the years we've been given with as much <u>vitality</u> as possible, rather than simply extending our years? When we invest in vitality enhancement measures, we are at the same time investing in long life development as well.

VITALITY

Vitality means to live life with zest and energy, to savor life, to enjoy life, to relish it, to inject vibrancy into everything we do. Vitality is a most personal concept; we each pursue it differently. Some mature adults find vitality by pursuing as active a lifestyle as they can; others find vitality by being more contemplative. Whatever strategy you choose will work for you as long as you feel you are expressing your true nature in a genuine way, and that you are aware that you are living with vitality. Perhaps the biggest part of vitality is one's awareness that one is living vitally right now – in the present. You can't live with vitality yesterday or tomorrow!

Vitality must be real; it can't be contrived or put on. It's much too easy in our sensationalizing and faultfinding world to take on a defeatist attitude about life in general. Such an attitude separates us from others, alienates us from ourselves, and breaks our communion with God; such an attitude is like poison to our vitality. With all the forces in our modern world that seem to tear us down, it's more important than ever to make vitality enhancement, living fully, and living positively top personal priorities.

Mature adults who actively pursue vitality:

1. **Have a high regard for themselves**. They seem to think favorably about themselves even in the face of trial and tribulation. They harbor an internal sense of "all rightness" at their core that appears undisturbed by outside pressures. Certainly they can become upset or irritable at times, but they regain composure rather quickly and emerge without damage to themselves.

2. **Value their physical health**. They monitor their body and are aware of their body's needs. They are kind to their body in the sense that they don't overtax it; they give it proper rest, grooming, exercise, medical attention, etc. They have realistic

expectations about what is appropriate for them at their stage of life.

3. **Have a high sense of personal worth.** They see themselves as valuable; they recognize their accomplishments as successes, and can easily understand how useful their work is to the overall project. They enjoy a high sense of utility; they believe that what they are doing is worthwhile.

4. **Have faith in themselves.** They understand at deep levels that they are capable, resourceful, and enduring. They enjoy an appropriate sense of personal confidence that is seldom, if ever, overstated. They seem to possess an aura of stability and security.

5. **Expect success.** They have a hard time believing in failure. What other people might call failure, they recognize as just another learning experience. They expect good things to happen right from the outset of a project or task.

6. **Enjoy productive and supportive relationships.** Perhaps because of their internal confidence, they enjoy people. They don't fear that they will be unfairly criticized, and if someone does become upset with them, they can handle the situation with appropriate social skill.

7. **Take optimal care of their body.** They like the feeling of knowing that they are doing what is necessary to keep the marvelous machine of their body in good running condition. They feed it correctly, get proper rest, maintain a regular exercise program, and perform other health

maintenance and promotion activities that allow them to perform maximally.

8. **Engage in stress reduction techniques.** Whether it's regular jogging, meditation, muscle relaxation, a power nap, prayer, soothing music, appropriate 'self-talk," or any number of other stress reduction techniques, they know several and use them regularly.

9. **Take good care of all their gifts.** They know their gifts and talents as an individual, and maintain an active interest in the development and growth of their talents. They seem to appreciate what they have been given and are not particularly envious of the talents and gifts of others.

10. **Make continuous adjustments to their attitudes and behaviors.** They seem to know innately that their attitudes are the bedrock of their personality and that they need to keep on top of which ones need modification and in what ways these modifications can be made. Attitudes can become antiques, useful yesterday, but quite out of function today. Sometimes we neglect to trade in our antique attitudes for newer, more functional models.

Vitality is akin to wellness, but much more. Vitality actually rests upon wellness. Wellness can be defined as "... the conscious and deliberate process by which people are actively involved in their overall well-being: intellectual, physical, social, emotional, occupational, and spiritual." (Hatfield & Hatfield). Wellness is the backdrop for vitality, but vitality is so much more immediate.

Vitality means …

- Injecting the present moment with its full measure of life and love.

- Searching for the spark that exists right here, right now!

- Being proactive, productive, positive, and spontaneous without being impulsive.

- Living to the fullest extent possible, under whatever conditions are presented to you.

- Finding the luster that exists in every situation: finding the love, finding the miracle.

- Grabbing the "gusto" that's always there.

Vitality means injecting the present moment with its full measure of life and love.

Vital living depends very little on the outside world and is almost entirely dependent upon one's internal world. People who live in poverty as well as in wealth can live with vitality. Even persons burdened with sickness can find vitality in their lives despite their hampered lifestyle. Persons living in a less-than-enhancing relationship can live with vitality, as can persons who live in a blissful relationship. Vitality is not blind to the circumstances of our lives; rather vitality is the force that helps us focus on what enhances us rather than what tears us down.

When Jesus' mother Mary spontaneously asked her son to attend to the unfortunate wine situation at the marriage feast at Cana, she was acting with vitality, seizing the moment for the good of all and allowing the spiritual gifts of Jesus to shine through. Perhaps this notion of allowing one's unique spiritual giftedness to shine through, no matter the circumstances of the moment, is at the center of vitality. We are called to express our giftedness, because it is here where we are "in touch" with God, acting in and for God.

WELLNESS: THE BACKDROP FOR VITALITY

Wellness can be seen as the backdrop for vitality. Wellness includes specific health-related tasks and processes:

1. **Disease Prevention.** We take active steps to prevent the onset of disease. We refrain from smoking and from over-consumption of food or alcohol. We wear seatbelts, eat balanced diets, and avoid inhaling or ingesting harmful fumes or carcinogens. Disease prevention includes being aware of our genetic risk factors and doing all we can to minimize known risk factors from making an appearance in our lives. If heart disease runs in the family, then risk factor controls such as exercise, fat intake reduction, stress control, taking low-dose aspirin regularly, etc., are preventive measures we can put in place. If cancer is in the family, proper diet, exercise, self-inspection, etc., are preventive risk control measures.

2. **Health Maintenance.** This refers to active steps we take to stay as healthy as possible. This includes following the seven basic health habits identified later in this chapter.

3. **Health Promotion.** This refers to the efforts to thrive, not simply survive. These would include a positive attitude about health, fitness, and wellness activities. Developing a personal health promotion plan and sticking to it is at the center of increasing wellness, follow-through, and well-being enrichment. Your health promotion plan is your personal mission statement for maximum human functioning.

Yet vitality goes beyond risk factor control, health maintenance, and health promotion.

Vitality is an intangible quality that demands full participation in the process we call life.

There is never a time in your life when you would allow yourself to think, *"OK, my health is shot, I can't do anything to influence my wellness, so I'll stop trying."* Such an attitude, and others like it, deny the vital forces inside of you, separate you from your very self, and deny the Spirit entry into your soul; you eventually become dry, lifeless, full of despair, and impotent.

Vitality enriches your life by rallying your own internal energies and focusing them onto the task at hand. Jesus asks us for conversion, for redemption, for change. So often we forget who we are: children of God on a holy mission here on this earth that leads us to God — our first source and center. When we discover our vitality, we also discover God within us. Vitality lets our light shine!

THE SEVEN BASIC HEALTH PRACTICES

There are seven areas of health practices. Together these seven contribute directly to your overall wellness and indirectly to your pursuit of vitality. These seven serve as the foundation for wellness, the backdrop for vitality:

1. **Avoid tobacco use.** Tobacco has no place in the life of a maturing person seeking lifespan vitality. The research is done, the data are in; there is no question that any type of tobacco use is clearly harmful and damaging to one's health. While it is true that some persons seem to have a higher tolerance to tobacco than others, it is indisputable that tobacco is detrimental to all those who use it regardless of their genetic makeup and tobacco sensitivity.

2. **Proper nutrition.** More, and more, and still more research arrives every day extolling the virtues of constructive dietary modifications. We all know to eat a balanced diet (to include at least five fruits and/or vegetables every day, to ingest six to eight glasses of water every day, to moderate our salt intake, to watch fats and oils, curb our use of red meat, etc., etc). Yet just because we know that these dietary habits are very useful, how many of us can say that we regularly follow them?

3. **Positive response to stress.** Each of us feels distress in different ways. What may be distress for some is actually a motivating challenge for others. We need to come to know our stressors and to devise constructive and healthful measures

to manage them, even convert them into life enhancers.

4. **Sufficient sleep and relaxation.** Some researchers maintain that since the invention of the light bulb, then television, and now the Internet, we have become a nation of sleep-deprived individuals. Sleep is rejuvenating, relaxing, and physically necessary. Each of us needs slightly different amounts of sleep, but we all need adequate sleep. Mature adults know their "sleep need" requirements and insure that they get what they need.

5. **Maintaining ideal weight.** Being overweight is perhaps the most disturbing risk factor in our culture. Fast food, rich food, fatty food, and too much food adds inches to our waistline, subtracts years from our life, and robs us of vitality.

6. **Moderate use of alcohol.** Recent research indicates that one ounce of alcohol per day for *most* persons is beneficial for their health. Yet, let's not make the mistake of thinking that since a little is good a lot is definitely better. Over two ounces of alcohol per day, for the average person, begins damaging the body rather than assisting it. The damage can be generalized, affecting all systems of the body; it can also be localized, as in inhibited liver function. Alcohol is also a depressant; over the long haul too much alcohol can deprive a person of their natural bodily and emotional rhythms, disrupting their mood and exciting anger.

7. **Sufficient exercise.** Our bodies need to move … they require ample exercise. Research indicates that 20 to 30 minutes of vigorous exercise, three to four times per week, is necessary to keep our bodies in good conditioning. Naturally, some persons, due to many factors, cannot exercise vigorously the way they would want; nonetheless, some exercise is almost always possible.

VITALITY BLOCKERS

Vitality emerges naturally as we nurture a mindset of living fully, and when potential wellness obstacles (or blockers) are removed. The following vitality blockers can prevent you from experiencing genuine vitality and from living fully. Dr. Norman Shealy, M.D. and Caroline Myss say in their book <u>The Creation of Health</u> that people can accelerate illness when one or more of the following eight dysfunctional patterns is present:

1. The presence of unresolved or deeply consuming emotional, psychological, or spiritual stress in our life. Holding a grudge, unresolved grief or anger, unexpressed feelings, resentments, injustices, abuse, and/or neglect can all stop us from experiencing vitality.

2. The inability to give or receive love. We all have the need to both receive *and* to give love. When either of these is blocked we "set ourselves up" for illness. Since these are "needs" this means that without fulfillment, at some level, we *will* get sick.

3. Lack of humor and the inability to distinguish serious concerns from the lesser issues of life. It's

been said that the most happy people are ones who "don't sweat the small stuff" in life and who believe that everything is "small stuff." We need to recognize that human behavior can be absurd, and instead of getting angry at it, allow our humor to find it amusing.

4. How effectively we exercise the power of choice and exercise positive influence over the movement and activities of our lives. So often we don't recognize that we *do* have the power of choice; we have options. I am always amazed at the number of intelligent persons who simply can't accept this notion. If we don't have options, if we don't have choices, then we are all trapped.

5. How well a person has attended to the needs of the physical body itself, i.e., nutrition, exercise, genetic makeup, and proper use of drugs or alcohol. We can misuse our body only so long before it gives us rather clear and unpleasant signals that all is not well.

6. How we deal with the "existential vacuum" that accompanies the absence or loss of meaning in our life. Maturing adult males, especially those who formerly held positions of responsibility or personal status that generated above-average success, are particularly vulnerable here.

7. The characteristics of people who become ill because of a tendency toward denial or circumstances or events that must be changed. Change is the watchword of the universe. All things must and do change; we must also change.

Unfortunately some of us cannot change ourselves; we simply let circumstances make decisions for us. This ensures pain and suffering, if not for us, then for others.

VITALITY ENHANCERS

Shealy and Myss go on to identify four core ingredients that define and determine the presence of wellness:

1. **Power.** We all face the task of finding an inner road leading to self-empowerment in our life journey. This inner road must be discovered and nurtured if wellness is to be achieved.

2. **Responsibility.** Each person must make the conscious decision to assume full responsibility for themselves if they are to live as "well" as can be.

3. **Wisdom.** Life teaches us many things; in fact, each moment is a learning moment we must decide to take advantage of. Wisdom and mindfulness in the present is the result.

4. **Love.** Each person who reaches a state of genuine wellness learns to give and receive love. People need to receive love and need to express it; without these we fail to thrive.

DEVELOPING HEALTH HABITS

A central part of wellness and well being, and of the ongoing emergence of vitality is constructing practices that assist your overall positive wellness and physical condition; we call these *positive health habits*. The opposite of these positive health habits are those practices that congeal into detrimental habits (or omissions) to your overall wellness and vitality. These we call *negative health habits.*

These habits develop as a consequence of your life history. Childhood events, your sickness history and your response to them, gradually teach lifestyle habits that can either bolster or detract from your health. Such daily practices as eating, walking, breathing, posture, use of medical care, and attitudes toward work and leisure each play a part in forging your health habits.

Most of us learn the major part of our health habit by modeling, i.e., we observe our parents (or others) performing behaviors that we ultimately adopt as our own. Early learning has a particularly strong impact upon us to the degree that we become imprinted with the behavior and adopt it as our own. This adoption process occurs ever so subtly; we hardly know we're doing it; it simply becomes a part of who and what we are. When this happens, we have developed a health habit, one that will eventually contribute to or detract from our overall wellness.

A personal health habit that affects my life to this day is the practice of having a sweet dessert after the evening meal. I feel that the evening meal is incomplete without something sweet to "top it off." Very rarely do we have a formal dessert after a weekday meal; nonetheless, I find myself scavenging through the pantry or refrigerator searching for that perfect "sweet tooth" satisfier. Try as I might to break this negative health habit, its perseverance seems bigger than me somehow. I often wonder where the strength of this habit comes from. It must be imprinted deeply, associated with a deep-seated primal need.

On the positive side, at another stage in my life I was exposed to regular physical exercise. At age 18 I went to my first U.S. Army summer "boot camp." Basic military training was the first time I experienced a rigorous, sustained, and regimented protocol of physical conditioning. At the end of the program I was 25 pounds lighter and in the best physical shape I'd even been in. I felt great, my self-esteem had risen immeasurably, and I had somehow proven to myself that I could influence my health, my body, and my life much more than I had previously thought. As a result, I developed a positive health habit of daily exercise. To this day, if I miss my exercise, I have a nagging feeling that something valuable is missing from my life.

INSIGHT QUESTIONS

1. How would you define wellness?

2. What is your personal "vitality quotient?" How vital of a life are you currently living?

3. Which is your strongest vitality enhancer? Vitality blocker?

4. Which is your strongest health practice (of the seven itemized)? Weakest?

5. What is one positive health habit that you learned from your parents? One negative health habit? Describe.

Chapter Two

Mastering the Psychology of Leisure

Mastering the Psychology of Leisure is the degree to which you have found personally satisfying endeavors that rejuvenate your body, or stimulate your mind, or enrich your spirit.

You may have never thought about it before, but leisure is a fundamental health enhancer. Having fun means that you can devise, pursue, and even master your own psychology of leisure. Leisure requires your active motivation, planning, organizing, and follow-through; it requires your proactive energies. Leisure is a manifestation of your inner self... a part of your own personal psychology, your own personality.

All leisure is not created equal. One person's leisure is another person's work. Some leisure activities sound anything but leisurely. Hang-gliding, bungee jumping, autocross racing, or even snowboarding are all great releases for some, but to others such activities sound only a heartbeat away from torture. Likewise, volunteering in a homeless shelter, delivering absentee ballots, cleaning "trashed" streams, or picketing for peace and justice issues can all be marvelously enriching and stimulating to some people, while others would categorize such activities as tedious at best. What, then, makes leisure... leisure?

First, let's look at the different categories of leisure. All leisure activities are generally seen as fitting into six categories:

1. **Social interaction.** Activities where you engage in interpersonal interchange of a fulfilling, satisfying nature. Activities ranging from simple, casual conversations to active and well-planned affairs such as galas, dances, parties, and social "get-togethers."

2. **Spectator Appreciation.** Activities where you watch others participate in any kind of activity. "People watching," sports events, musical concerts, parade viewing, and many, many other spectator engagements would qualify for this leisure category.

3. **Creative Expression.** Any activity that "taps into" your unique creativity. This would include all artistic endeavors to include everyday kinds of things such as: how you cook your eggs; how you care for your car; how you mow the lawn; how you talk, walk, and dress; and even how you pray. Creative expression includes all that you do which

bears the indelible mark of your own personal creativity.

4. **Intellectual Stimulation**. Activities that enhance your mind. These would include anything from reading, studying computer manuals, "surfing" the Internet, watching educational TV programs, attending a lecture, intently following current events, having a stimulating conversation, listening to self-help audiotapes... the possibilities are endless.

5. **Physical Exercise.** Any and all activities that cause you to move your body parts. This can be organized and purposeful activity like a game of tennis, or walking the local mall, working out at the gym, training for a marathon, cycling across town, paddling a kayak, even flying a kite can all be seen as physical exercise. In addition, this category of leisure would include physical activity associated with your activities of daily living as long as you were mindful of the leisure quality inherent in the activity.

6. **Solitary Relaxation**. Activities done alone, from just sitting and rocking, to bird watching, jogging, taking a solo walk, knitting by yourself, to a relaxing bath. Being alone can be quiet leisure and profoundly relaxing, rejuvenating, enriching, and rewarding.

LEISURE: A FUNDAMENTAL HUMAN NEED

Leisure is a human need; without it we eventually get sick. Some of us need generous amounts of leisure, while others of us need only a relative fraction, but all of us need leisure to some personally satisfying degree. Leisure is indeed a need!

> *If we work hard enough, long enough without a break, without a respite, and without the soothing balm of leisure, we <u>will</u> get sick.*

When we have no leisure, we risk a gradual erosion of our genuine human spirit. Leisure fills those empty spaces that emerge in us as we engage in our work. Leisure settles our bodies after concentrated or tedious activity has gradually raised our internal tension. Leisure relieves the built-up pressure caused by our use, and sometimes overuse, of our physical and mental faculties. Leisure unwinds those thousands of rubber band-like life strands that can become tightly coiled and even knotted as a result of prolonged exertion. Leisure offers us respite in a world which otherwise demands too much.

LEISURE AND STRESS

Leisure has several paradoxes; it operates seemingly the opposite from the way our common sense would expect it to act. For example, when we are stressed we seem to require more leisure as a respite than at other less stressed times in our lives. We are all well aware that stress can come from being overloaded with things to do and pressures from the press of a harried pace. Yet few people realize that stress can also come from living a lifestyle that is *under*-loaded. Studies have shown that prolonged inactivity can give rise to stress in our lives just as easily as over-activity can.   Under-stimulation in our lives; underutilization of our God-given gifts, talents, and personal resources can be a source of stress for us and require that we remedy such an imbalance in our lives with leisure.

In our maturing years, leisure usually commands a more central position in our lives than it did previously. Whereas in years past we saw our work as the central cohesive factor in our lives, in our maturing years leisure is normally raised to a more elevated status.   In our retirement years, leisure receives more of our life energy than it had received throughout our work lives, perhaps more than it had received since our childhood.

Leisure generally becomes more important for us in our maturing years.

The manner, the style, and the intensity of our leisure endeavors are different than we experienced during our full-time working years.

LEISURE: ALWAYS A DIVERSION

In our full-time working years, our central life cause was, for most folks, earning a living, and/or supporting a family, even if that family was a unit of only one or two. Leisure allows us to rebalance our lives, which can become "off-kilter," "out-of-round," and/or generally "lopsided" with work. Herein lies the heart of leisure, the central truth about leisure that must be present for any activity to actually be considered leisure. In order for any activity to be leisure it must fulfill two criteria. It must: 1) be physically rejuvenating, and/or mentally stimulating, and/or spiritually enriching, and 2) <u>it must be diversionary</u> from one's normal work. We can sometimes forget this second criterion: leisure cannot be leisure unless it is separate from work *and* a diversion from work.

This diversionary quality of leisure can create a snag for retirees. First, retirees may have no work. Second, many retirees may believe that the purpose of retirement is *for* living a life of leisure. How can one have a leisure lifestyle without leisure? This appears to be a grand contradiction in terms. Indeed, here is a leisure paradox: leisure must always take a secondary position in our life; there must always be some type of work, or what we could call "life cause" activities in a person's life for them to fully appreciate, enjoy, and gain from their leisure pursuits.

Leisure serves us because it gives us pause from the central cause of our life.

When leisure activities become your full-time endeavor, then your leisure becomes your work; it ceases to be your leisure. When this happens, the power of the leisure activity, whatever it may be, is disemboweled. The rejuvenating, stimulating, and enriching potency that the leisure activity would otherwise have for you is gutted when you have no balancing activities in your life which you regard as your life's work. The paradox of leisure is that in order to enjoy leisure you must have some type of work in your life, some type of activity from which leisure can be a diversion.

During your active working years, your work-dominated years, the balance between work and leisure was clearly tilted toward work. You expended much more energy at work than at leisure. In your maturing years, and especially your retirement years, for most of us this balancing has reversed itself. Generally we spend much less energy on work-related issues and more on leisure-related ones. Nonetheless it would prove counterproductive for any retiree to devote their full-time energies to leisure because their life would not be balanced. Their leisure would cease to be diversionary, and would therefore cease to genuinely feed them in body, mind, and spirit.

THE SPIRITUAL SIDE OF LEISURE

While some maturing adults consume their lives with leisure activities, essentially forfeiting themselves to leisure as they formerly did to work, other maturing adults, even people of faith, fail to see that leisure is a valuable human endeavor at all. We need to recognize our personal leisure needs and act on them if we hope to achieve maximal health and wellness in our retirement years. When we depreciate our leisure needs we discount our own sense of self. When we depreciate our leisure needs, we lose sight of our true nature and we risk falling prey to the attitude that we live to work; that our worth rests in our work alone. Such an attitude is not of Jesus Christ.

Leisure reminds us that our sole purpose
in life is not simply to do but to be.

When we recognize fully that we are first and foremost a child of God, a spiritual being; when we gradually come to appreciate our essential self as a spiritual, Holy Self that is currently resident in a human, material body, we can begin

29

to move away from a definition of ourselves as an achievement/production machine and move closer toward a more balanced, accurate, and God-reliant definition of self. As we transform ourselves away from work as the chief definer of our life, we can come to see our leisure interests and pursuits as part of our faith journey, as a condition of the soul. In this sense, leisure helps build in us a sense of wholeness, because we grow to realize that our spiritual nature is *the* cohesive and binding force in our lives. It's that force which gives integrity to our world and balance to our lives.

Leisure is more than simply performing activities that please us. Leisure includes a contemplative mode of internal perception, a looking inward as well. This internal leisure allows us to rediscover our childlike qualities. Where you find <u>awe, and wonder, and delight</u> is also where you find a special leisure that refreshes the spirit, and is a wellspring of rejuvenation for us. When we do this — when we find awe, wonder, and delight in a childlike way — we can better see God's creations for what they truly are. Sr. Marie Therese Ruthmann said the *"celebration of things as they are is the soul of leisure."*

> *Life without leisure creates a bleak psychological landscape within you.*

Life without leisure renders you spiritually anemic. Leisure bears gifts in abundance; gifts that you would probably not receive from any other source. Some of leisure's gifts are: motivation, creativity, exercise, entertainment, relaxation, self-confidence, and socialization. When we escalate leisure to the spiritual level, we see that leisure becomes even more generous. Leisure provides meaningful roles; it offers opportunities for making important contributions; it has the potential for transforming lifestyles, and it creates the capacity to serve others. All these are gifts from the heart, gifts given freely by a gift-giver who cares most deeply about us.

If we cannot resolve the challenge of leisure during our maturing years, we face some dismal consequences. We find it almost impossible to reflect on the true meaning of living. Our life degenerates into a shallow routinized "to do" list for accomplishing things and performing tasks. With such a mindset, we find it difficult to truly appreciate the beauty and the loveliness of the present moment. We can become callous, anxious, self-centered, and self-absorbed when we fail to meet our leisure needs. Developing a leisure attitude gives us the pause to be grateful, and in the process, leisure grants serenity.

JESUS AND LEISURE

One intriguing question for contemplation is: Did Jesus participate in leisure? Did Jesus balance his inherent humanness with leisure activities, or did his divinity somehow not require leisure?

In the Genesis version of how God made the heavens and earth, God rested on the seventh day, and obvious reference to the rejuvenating power of leisure, rest for the body (Genesis 2:2-3). Jesus is recorded time and again as going away from the crowd for prayer. Can prayer be considered leisure? When prayer gives us pause to remember our most accurate sense of our true self, it clearly qualifies as leisure. Certainly this is not "idle leisure." So-called "idle leisure" is a misnomer. There is no such thing as idle leisure; by definition leisure is purposeful. Idle leisure refers then to simple time filling, or more precisely, time wasting, and occupies no place in true leisure.

Jesus once welcomed his apostles and disciples back from missionary work where they had toiled long, two by two, preaching, teaching, and converting Jew and Gentile alike, with:

> *"Come away to a deserted place all by yourselves and rest a while.' For many were coming and going, and they had no leisure even to eat." (Luke 6:31).*

We have no record of Jesus engaging in leisure activities such as games or sports, although as a boy it would seem quite natural that he would have been so inclined. Yet it would appear that he was well acquainted with human interaction, regardless of how much time he engaged in it himself. We could assume that Jesus' interaction was always with some instructive purpose, that he focused his discussion on his earthly task. Yet Jesus was human as well as divine, and we know he had friends (Lazarus, Martha, and Mary to name only a few). It would therefore seem safe to assume that at least a portion of his social interaction was inclined toward relationship building rather than instruction, and could therefore be considered leisure. It seems rather hard, if not impossible, to conceive of any human being as totally devoid of leisure of some kind.

PAST LEISURE ACTIVITY

Our leisure preferences and interests change over our lifespan. It's most interesting to note these changes because they give us a grand overview of our leisure "career" and may help us better utilize and express our leisure needs now, in our maturing years.

Each decade of your life generally has some leisure theme, some central focus that serves as the cohesive agent for your leisure activities during that decade. Naturally, each of us expresses this central theme in different ways; your personality will always move your toward expressing the 'real you' in ways which serve to differentiate you from all others. There are no two people who play the same game or the same activity in the same way; each will be slightly different in their approach, their intensity, their style, and even their goals. Leisure is one of the fundamental ways through which we express our uniqueness. The following decades contain words and phrases that may serve to jog your memory.

1. **Childhood, ages 1-10**. Play, toys, playmates, learning through play, self play, sports, Scouts, Brownies, 4-H, school play, movies, family functions.

2. **Teens, ages 11-20**. Sports, free-time with friends, play places, "hangouts," Saturday nights, travel, driving, dates, humor, summer vacations, social, civic, religious organizations, secrets.

3. **Twenties, ages 21-30**. Leisure time partners, entertainment, travel, leisure purchases, value of leisure, active or sedentary leisure, work vs. play balance.

4. **Thirties, ages 31-40**. Patterns of leisure, "rest" leisure, leisure experiments, philosophy of leisure, leisure for health, spectator leisure, favorite movies, favorite "playthings," days of rest.

5. **Forties, ages 41-50**. Leisure dreams, leisure goals, fun, reading material, study, physical activity, "down time," personal refreshment, vacations.

6. **Fifties, ages 51-60**. Social involvement, classes, more or less time for leisure, personal meaning, leisure "buddies," cost of leisure, favorite movies, holidays, Saturday nights.

7. **Sixties, ages 61-70**. Changes in leisure, develop new leisure skills, classes or causes, risks, volunteering, new leisure areas, creativity, community and/or religious involvement, travel highlights.

8. **Seventies, ages 71-80**. Leisure companions, new leisure, shift in energy level, enjoy fun, courses, creativity, travel, personal meaning, prayer.

9. **Eighties plus, ages 81 plus**. Singing, reading, card playing, games, prayer, socialization, leisure and sickness.

Leisure loses its luster when it takes the full-time center stage position in your life.

Like a vacation spot loses some of its luster when you make it your permanent home because it is no longer an escape or a diversion from your everyday world, so too the same leisure activities that formerly gave pleasure cease to provide the same refreshment, stimulation, and enrichment when leisure becomes your full-time pursuit. You may wonder how some retirees can play golf every day, or go fishing every day, or simply rest every day, or do any leisure activity every day and still gain pleasure and satisfaction from it. The truth is that they have simply replaced one job with another, one habitual action with another. The same beliefs, attitudes, and values that drove them at work, continue to drive them at their new "work". Even though they appear to have shifted their lives dramatically, moving from full-time work to full-time golf, all they really have done is to transfer their values from one activity to another without changing them.

Mature persons need balance in their lives to be as well as possible. They may need to augment their lives with greater meaning and purpose by adding their own life cause, their new work to their mix of activities. As "All work and no play makes Jack (or Jill) a dull boy (or girl)" so too, all play and no work can do the same.

MAKING ROOM FOR HOLY FUN

One aspect of leisure that is often overlooked is your ability to have fun. Fun is defined as: 1) what provides amusement or enjoyment, and 2) a mood for finding or making amusement. Fun as a verb is defined: To indulge in banter or play as in a joke. Fun implies a certain level of humor, and humor can be defined as: 1) the mental faculty of discovering, expressing, or appreciating the ludicrous or absurdly incongruous, 2) something that is designed to be comical or amusing. Some leisure activities can be fun, while others seem to provide satisfactions not specifically requiring fun; their purpose is something other than having fun.

Fun allows a certain detachment or abandonment of self. In a sense we surrender ourselves; we let go of ourselves when we experience fun. Time monitoring ceases to the point that we can lose track of time when we're having fun. Fun removes us from our everyday world by suspending it temporarily, so we can make room for humor.

Each of us seems to require varying amounts of fun.

Some of us have high fun needs; we seem to crave fun while others of us don't share this same fun-need level. In whatever levels we require fun, having fun does seem to have a decidedly positive impact upon our overall wellness status. Maturing adults who report higher levels of fun in their lives also report higher levels of life satisfaction as well; they are happier!

When we apply the concept of fun to our spirituality, we come up with the seemingly strange concept of "holy fun." Fun may seem somewhat opposed to the fundamental thrust of spirituality, yet it is quite possible, and even wellness enhancing, to keep a good sense of humor even with God. How many times did Jesus remind us to "*be of good cheer*" and to "*fear not*"? The virtue of joy certainly includes some strands of fun and humor tucked into its fabric. I've seen several artistic renderings of Jesus where he appears to be laughing heartily.

All this gives rise to the supposition that we are not to go around morose, emotionally flaccid, and living in fear. On the contrary, we're invited to reflect the joy and the light of Christ, to express the noblest parts of ourselves, to be involved in the full passion of life, to live life abundantly, and to love one another. Certainly, then, we are to display a healthy sense of humor and have "holy fun."

Another aspect of "holy fun" is to develop the mental faculty of discovering, expressing, or appreciating what is ludicrous or absurdly incongruous about the human condition. We say we are people of peace and yet we always seem to find ways of waging war on both geopolitical levels, and on personal levels as well. We support the idea of love but find it difficult to express love in its various forms and levels. We claim to be people of justice yet we find it hard to "turn the other cheek" in mercy. Indeed with each and every virtue, the human condition manages to find and exploit its shadow, the places where the virtue is absent. We also take our holy giftedness and use it not for God's purposes but for our own.

One response to these human foibles is to berate them, bemoan them, and to eventually lapse into some state of despair. Such a state is primarily regressive and inactive; it's a far cry from building up the kingdom of God. On the other hand, our response could be one of "holy fun." Internally shaking our heads in laughter and amusement at the childish qualities that seem to permeate our beings, rather than shaking our heads in disgust. Perhaps the first step toward finding the motivation is to get out there in Jesus' vineyards and work to build up the kingdom so it can more clearly reflect the love of God, rather than standing back only to render furtive attacks that serve no earthly or heavenly purpose.

INSIGHT QUESTIONS

1. Which one of the six categories of leisure is your favorite? Least favorite?

2. When might you have ever experienced an erosion of your essential human spirit because of a lack of leisure? Describe.

3. What are your most satisfying leisure pursuits?

4. How would you say leisure is associated with your health?

5. Where might you experience awe, wonder, and delight?

Chapter Three

Taking Charge of Your Life

*Taking Charge of Your Life is the degree
to which you engage in responsible self-
health care actions designed to raise or
maintain your overall level of health so
that optimal physical wellness can
naturally emerge in our life.*

What are the factors that allow some individuals to seek
responsibility for their own health and wellness, while
others seem stuck in inactivity? Why do some individuals
quite naturally and smoothly assume health-seeking
behaviors, while others seem "health asleep?" The first
step toward positive self-health care responsiveness is
your awareness and understanding of health promotion
behaviors.

How adept, resourceful, and conscientious are you in
pursuing your own wellness? What actions allow your

wellness to grow? What action might stifle your wellness? Can you overdo your self-health care actions? What is an effective balance between helping yourself and seeking professional advice for your health concerns?

For self-health care actions to be responsible they must be:

1. **Reliable.** The self-health care action can be used over and over again with confidence.

2. **Valid.** The self-health care action works where, how, and in the way that you want it to work.

3. **Informed.** The self-health care action stands on a solid base of research or experience.

4. **Appropriate.** The self-health care action fits the situation well, it isn't too powerful nor is it too weak.

THE NECESSITY FOR CHANGE: INDIVIDUAL SELF-HEALTH CARE RESPONSIBILITY SKILLS

Perhaps the foremost behavior that allows maturing adults to move toward positive self-health care is a general awareness of shifting health requirements as your body marches on its journey of maturation. Blindness or denial of the fact of the impact maturation has upon your physical functioning can muzzle any hope of garnering new and enhanced perspectives of your own self-health care needs. Change is necessary over the entire lifespan. Over time we change our relationship with our bodies and our sense of who we are.

FOUR COMPETENCIES OF SELF-HEALTH CARE RESPONSIVENESS

1. **Assertiveness.** Self-health care responsibility means learning and practicing skills that aid your health and wellness. One of these skills is *assertiveness.* Self-health care assertiveness means becoming intensely engaged in self-directed actions supporting your own health and physical wellness. Assertiveness means being able to state what you need and that you consequently want to achieve optimal health. You must be able to clearly state your preferences to yourself. Once you have them clarified, you can then communicate them to others. Part of assertiveness is to 'own" or embrace your own health care needs; to communicate those needs to the person or persons who need to know; and then to actively work to actually incorporate the needs into reality.

2. **Establishing Priorities.** Another self-health care responsibility skill is *establishing priorities.* Some things are simply more important than others; our health and wellness need to be very high on our priority list. We know certain things about optimal functioning. We live best when we are healthy. Living a healthy life is not simply a matter that takes care of itself; it requires our active participation, our deliberate actions to live as artfully as possible. Giving health and wellness a clear priority in your life demands close and careful scrutiny of all the arenas of your life, with an eye toward truly enjoying life the way a wine connoisseur enjoys fine wine. Your life is like a piece of art that you are working on each day.

We need to live our lives as connoisseurs, choosing each task, each food, each thought, and each behavior with great care and consideration.

3. **Relaxed Lifestyle.** A third self-health care responsibility skill is learning to relax. More accurately, it's *learning how to live a relaxed lifestyle.* In the last chapter you learned how to master the psychology of leisure, yet living a relaxed lifestyle means more than being leisurely, it also means becoming as centered as possible, and as mindful of your presence in the moment as possible. Developing such a perspective frees you from the tyranny of thinking you are not doing enough for your health.

4. **Attitude about Discomfort.** The fourth self-health care responsibility skill is *developing a new attitude about discomfort.* Discomfort is a part of living. There exists no discomfort-free state of existence on this earth. This may be the discomfort of gastric upset, or chronic arthritis pain, or emotional pain, or joint stiffness, or any of a vast array of physical imperfections that you encounter as a result of living. Discomfort is felt at a subjective level; no one feels discomfort exactly as you do, everyone experiences it differently. Some persons can learn to live with a level of discomfort that would completely hobble other persons. The question is to what degree can you take-on the responsibility for the discomfort in your own life? To what degree can you shift your perspective about the

many discomforts in your life away from discomfort-causing debilitation and toward invigorating functionality?

PERSONALITY AND SELF-HEALTH CARE

As people mature, one thing seems clear: they become more different from one another.

As personal history nudges us, and environmental changes push us, family structure, occupational diversity, genetic makeup, and many other factors converge over time and interact with your unique personality to create the distinct *you* that you are today. There are many ways to address personality differences, but I like the Berkeley Growth Study classifications of styles of retirement living, because we can align <u>self-health responsiveness</u> with the five personality styles rather compactly.

1. **Mature.** A mature personality is one that takes self-health care seriously in the sense that they value their health and wellness as a clear priority. Maturing persons treat themselves as responsible adults; they shoulder the actions necessary for constructive modifications in their lifestyle and make solid considered choices. They generate alternatives for thriving and take responsibility for making these happen. In short, they foster constructive change in their lives.

2. **Rocking Chair.** Rocking-chair personalities believe that their maturing years are for resting. They take notice of their health only when pressed by stark

discomfort to do so. They are passive in their responsiveness toward behavioral modifications that could improve, enrich, or enhance their health. They seem to live by the adage, "Whatever will be will be."

3. **Armored.** Armored personalities are rather "uptight" about their health. They may be constantly vigilant about what could be going wrong with their body. They tend to overreact to discomfort and consult professional health care providers more than necessary. They over-define their health and may overdo exercise, dieting, and become a bit compulsive about health issues.

4. **Self-Haters.** The so-called self-haters are actually depressed at some level. Because of this they may either over-inflate their health concerns or do just the opposite. In their search for reasons why they feel badly, they may alight on their bodies as the focus of their attention and think that their bodies are malfunctioning when actually they are physically OK. They may become somewhat hypochondriacal; or they may feel so badly that they neglect their health.

5. **Angry.** The angry personality generally shuns professional health care in deference to its own. Rather than seeing their overall health and wellness as a partnership between themselves and professional health care providers, they discount and even distrust professionals and consequently shoulder their health management by themselves,

only consulting professionals when something traumatic occurs.

DISORDERS OF SELF-HEALTH CARE MOTIVATION

1. **Belief in myths about maturation and health.** Somewhere in our culture's quest for the holy grail of health, and especially after constructing the most sophisticated and most effective medical care system on the face of the earth, we may find ourselves attached to a dangerous belief that *quality* health care is measured in terms of the amount or *quantity* of health care we receive. This belief may have burrowed so deeply into our belief core that it now borders on a myth – something we believe but which simply isn't true.

2. Another health care myth which seems to have emerged in our highly organized medical community is that we must *receive* health care from professionals in all situations, rather than be more selective of those times when it would be most prudent giving it to ourselves. Such a notion seems to defer the responsibility for your health to the "wisdom" of your medical caregivers. Certainly, we must place our trust in the knowledge and the competence of our health care providers, yet we can carry this notion to a most illogical and distorted extension when we somehow unknowingly assume that our health care is their responsibility, not our own.

3. Both these myths can work against our quest for optimal health. They have special impact upon the lives of maturing adults who, as a group, interact

more frequently with the medical care community than other age groups. When these two myths become embedded into our belief core we can abdicate our health care almost completely to health care professionals. Such a situation invades the psychological sense of self that is requisite for optimal functioning; robs the maturing adult of self-care decision making; and perhaps pushes us to a self-care infantilization where the adult fails to exercise a healthy level of self-determination. Each of these consequences can split maturing adults from themselves in ways that diminish their vitality.

4. **Wrong expectations and perceptions of health.** Perhaps the biggest expectation about health and wellness that acts as a stumbling block for maturing adults is the momentum of their previous lifestyle. We somehow frame our health in terms of what it was yesterday: *My health was fine yesterday, so it will be today and tomorrow as well.* Such a health perspective serves only to block needed healthy changes as we mature. Because we were healthy yesterday, we keep the same eating, exercise, lifestyle, sleep, etc., patterns that we used yesterday. We become blind to the need for lifestyle and attitudinal change. We fail to recognize and integrate changes in our own body and changes of health status of our friends and family around us. We fail to see ourselves any differently than we did yesterday.

5. **Distorted thinking about self-health care.** Our thinking includes our assessments, our opinions,

and our judgments about our health as well as the mix between self-care and professional care. Our thinking can bring us down a path where we over-rely on professional health care personnel, with the thought, "I really shouldn't take care of myself medically." On the other hand, our thinking may do the opposite. We may overinflate the value of our own self-health care, like the woman who solely with mega-doses of vitamin E.

6. **Dispirited feeling about self-health care.** Dispirited feeling refers to a sense of insufficiency or inadequacy of self that leads to an overreliance on health care professionals: "I'm not good enough," or "I can never do the right thing," and other such feelings about our own effectiveness can hamper self-health care behavior.

7. **Decision blocks.** Decisions require options, and options are not generated in a vacuum. Information is needed to make the kind of considered choices regarding health care that lead to the desired outcomes. For maturing adults facing physical changes as never before, the array of alternatives may seem overwhelming at times. The only alternative that seems likely is to seek professional assistance, and clearly that may be the wisest choice in most cases, but certainly not in all.

FACTORS OF SELF-HEALTH CARE RESPONSIVENESS

Personal responsibility starts with self-awareness and a heightened sense of what's around you, i.e., the interplay of your own needs together with the impact of your environment upon those needs. As your body changes, so do the needs of that body. Some of these needs make an obvious appearance in your life: sensitivity of all five senses, strength and speed of reaction time, need for strength recuperation, need for pacing, more need for rest. Other physical needs are not as clear: nutrition and hydration need modifications, stature and flexibility changes, gradual wearing of joints, chronic hypertension, metabolic changes, medication interaction incidents, sleep quality interruptions, exercise requirements, and many others.

These changes call for a level of self-health care responsibility not before encountered. This emerging responsibility requires new personal initiatives.

1. **A renewed commitment to the issue of health.** As your body matures you're forced to give it more attention, support, and even assistance as you make your way through your activities of daily living. Health modifications of all sorts are necessary. Most of us have sustained an injury of some dimension in our lives and have experienced the need to make temporary shifts in the way we do things. Others have had surgery that required prolonged recuperation and even physical rehabilitation. Yet the specter of physical modifications on a more or less permanent basis may send shock waves through us as never before.

2. **Conscious intention to make the environment of life better as we mature.** Many maturing adults blessed with robust health to date have paid scant attention to their health; their bodies have always responded very well to all required demands.

Consequently such persons may be unprepared for the modifications in self-health care necessary as the maturation process progresses. Other maturing adults simply deny that changes are taking place and may unconsciously take steps to either cover up or sidestep the modifications necessary in their lives.

3. **Engagement in the preparation steps necessary to smooth the way toward improved or sustained health.** Once your health consciousness has been sufficiently raised, and you have developed a firm intention to address your own health from a more formal standpoint, it's then time to begin developing options for improved health on a physical level. Many maturing adults seem dumbfounded when asked to generate self-health care options that could raise their overall level of wellness. Yet we can't hope to actually change our lives until we have some structured alternatives and enter into a decision-making process of considered choices.

4. **Involvement or participation in the work necessary to make improved or sustained health a reality.** This means we actually need to take some action. Action may be the biggest obstacle facing so many maturing adults. Let's try to break this action step down a bit:

Action Model

	Situation that can be Influenced	Situation that cannot be Influenced
Decide to Take Action	MASTERY	Ceaseless Striving
Decide not to Take Action	Give up	CREATIVE ACCEPTANCE

When we apply this action model to self-health care behaviors, we can see there are only two of the four quadrants that sustain wellness. These are: quadrant one, "Mastery" where something can be changed and we decide to take action; and quadrant four, "Creative Acceptance" where there is no action that can influence the outcome and we wisely and healthfully decide not to take action. Quadrants two, "Ceaseless Striving," and three, "Giving Up" are clearly not responsible courses of action. Ceaseless striving leads to ineffective action by using the same methods over and over that never worked in the first place, while Giving-up leads to a paralyzing inactivity in the face of the clear possibility that some action could have a positive impact.

SELF-HEALTH CARE MOTIVATION

Some years ago, the world-famous distance runner Jim Fixx died of heart failure while running a "routine" 10-mile jog. Jim Fixx was known in the running world as a prolific writer and marvelous personal motivator of other runners. He advocated running as a central component of a highly healthy lifestyle. His loss was felt deeply in the running community.

There were some who pointed to Jim Fixx's death as a morbid testimony to their supposition that one's health status is locked up in one's genes, that one's genetic heritage blindly determines all physical eventualities. They were quick to claim that Jim Fixx's running did him no good. "Look at what happened to him," they asserted, "dead at age 54!" Running, they argued, not only didn't help him, it actually may have hastened his death. They used his unfortunate death simply to buttress their own belief in a rather passive approach to health and wellness.

Actually, Jim Fixx was taking great self-health care responsibility. His family was prone to heart disease. His father died very young of heart failure, and his brother died at age 38 of the same ailment. Certainly these events, and the underlying meaning of them, served to motivate Jim Fixx to modify his lifestyle and adopt running as a means of dealing with his familial trait of early heart disease. Once the true facts of his family history were made more public, it became obvious that Jim Fixx had actually prolonged his life *and* had immeasurably enriched it along the way by incorporating running into his lifestyle. Jim Fixx had taken positive self-health care responsibility; he exhibited a high degree of positive self-health care responsiveness.

This story of Jim Fixx strikes close to my own heart both literally and figuratively. My own family history is similar to Jim Fixx's. When one of my younger brothers died suddenly at the age of 47 of heart disease some years ago, I was certainly motivated to change some of my self-health care behaviors. Since my paternal grandfather died of heart disease at age 50 and my own father died of the same ailment at age 57, I've been actively exercising regularly since my 20s.

When my own brother died however, I not only strengthened my exercise program, but I also significantly changed my diet, added vitamins (especially antioxidants), and now make more regular visits to my doctor. I was motivated, much like Jim Fixx. Certainly it's my hope (and expectation) that these new self-health care behaviors will have a positive effect on my life duration and enjoyment, as they did for Jim Fixx.

Self-Health Care Motivation: Positive and Negative

Success is an outcome of motivation in action. Motivation is the driving force behind any and all genuine successes. Motivation is as complex as you are. It's the sum total of your needs, desires, values, and plans, whether these are conscious or unconscious. You may have a desire to learn to play golf, or write a book, or change your life. In order to accomplish these goals you must become actively motivated.

Motivation has three components:

1. **Achievement Motivation:** The tendency to achieve success. How driven are you to get to where you want to go? This trait is evenly distributed in the population; some people have an abundance of achievement motivation; others

have little. Achievement motivation can be developed.

2. **Probability of Success:** How likely is it that you will achieve success in any given role? When tasks are perceived as having either a very high or very low probability for success, then the tendency to achieve success is low. Your tendency to achieve success is most strongly aroused by tasks perceived as having an intermediate probability of success.

3. **Relative Attractiveness of Success:** What's in it for me? What are my rewards? This motivation quality is also known as the incentive value.

The kind of motivation so far described is positive motivation, defined as the tendency to achieve success. There is another type of motivation, however, called *negative motivation,* which is defined as the tendency to avoid failure. Rarely can you identify tasks that are clearly either all positively or all negatively motivated. Usually there are elements of both present, creating an internal struggle with every task attempted. One side of you says, *"Yes, go ahead with it; succeed!"* The other side of you says, *"No, don't try it; you may fail!"* But a failure would be embarrassing personally and socially, so your motivation for the task is one of avoiding failure. It is enlightening to identify which motive is strongest in you -- the motivation to achieve success or the motivation to avoid failure.

INTERNAL AND EXTERNAL MOTIVATION

Motivation can also be classified as either internal or external. Internal motivation is when you are driven by your own intrinsic motive power, personal curiosity, or desire to achieve. External motivation is when you are driven by the desire to win approval from others or simply comply with authority or tradition. Much of our action is externally motivated; in our complex and regulated world, it is hard to the point of impossible to escape.

You're externally motivated when your primary goal for wellness is to "look good." You're internally motivated when your goal for wellness is to "feel good."

If you can clearly identify the areas in your life where you're internally motivated, you have unearthed a descriptive bit of information that can be most useful.

All of us want success, but how do we get it? To achieve success, you need to clearly identify what you want, set goals that allow you to start on your road to success, and most importantly, implement these goals in your everyday life. You must also recognize that with success comes responsibility. Part of success is to be willing to shoulder this responsibility. This is sometimes difficult!

DEVELOPING A SELF-HEALTH CARE PLAN

To move forward with responsible self-health care actions; you need a goal, a purpose, a direction, and a desired consequence that you wish to achieve.

Your first step in developing a self-health care plan is to identify the three most threatening medical problems that you're currently dealing with, or those you might expect in the future. What are your most potentially damaging medical risk factors? For me the three would be: 1) Heart disease, 2) Depression, and 3) Stroke. These constitute my three top health risks.

Heart disease has played a traumatic role in my family, both on my paternal and maternal sides. Depression, even in very small amounts, is something I have noticed can rob me of my vitality and my determination to be the best that I can be. Depression can separate me from those whom I love and cause the zest in my life to erode. Stroke or cerebral hemorrhage took my maternal grandmother and one of my aunts; it too then is a clear risk factor for me. Each of these three can potentially disrupt my life on a grand scale. I need to construct a self-health care plan that is primarily directed toward these three health risk issues.

Your second step is to gather facts, information, and dates. I need reliable, valid, and appropriate information about these three health risk issues. Where can I get such information? Certainly I can "*Google*" these or even check my local library or bookstore as places to start my search. I can contact the American Heart Association, the Mental Health Association, or the American Stroke Prevention Association. I might contact my local hospital - they may have support groups or classes on these topics. Naturally, I can also consult my doctor about my concerns.

As I assimilate all this information, I begin to identify ways and means of prevention. The information I have gathered is sure to outline specific actions that may allow me to lower or lessen the severity of the risk of these three points of wellness vulnerability. I can collect these suggestions and organize them into goal statements for my overall health and well being.

Now I can integrate these organized health risk prevention goals into my lifestyle. I need to actually write them down, decide where they can be logically placed in my daily life, and then find the motivation to perform them regularly and consistently.

INSIGHT QUESTIONS

1. In general, how responsive are you to your own self-health care?

2. How proficient are you with...

   a. Health assertiveness?

   b. Establishing healthcare priorities?

   c. Living a relaxed lifestyle?

   d. Dealing with discomfort?

3. What disorders in thinking regarding your self-health care might you suffer from?

4. Which of the four factors of self-health care responsiveness are you most comfortable with? Which do you practice the best? Worst?

5. What motivates your self-health care?

6. Have you constructed a self-care plan? Describe it.

Chapter Four

Continuous Health Self-Improvement: Enhancing (Not Simply Maintaining) Your Own Health

Continuous Health Self-Improvement is the degree to which you regularly see yourself on an ongoing health improvement program constructed to enhance your capacity for fullness of living.

As your body matures and you add years to your life, your physical form quite naturally becomes more vulnerable to maladies of all kinds. How does your faith life factor into your efforts to remain as vital, vibrant, and as healthy and well as possible?

Chronic sickness seems the bane of most mature adults. In fact, fully 86% of Americans over the age of 65 have at least one chronic ailment that limits their activities of daily living to some degree. Health maintenance takes up larger and larger "chunks" of our energy. Yet our health-related goals in our maturing years need to be focused beyond health maintenance and onto health promotion and health improvement. This is not a health "pipe dream;" it is possible and even necessary if we are to live our lives to the fullest.

The response of a mature adult to chronic sickness cannot be a response of passivity, submission, or resignation. A chronic sickness does not exempt maturing adults (and younger ones too) from being as well as they possibly can; on the contrary, having a chronic sickness is cause for even higher levels of self-health care motivation so one can achieve the highest levels of wellness.

There is a spirituality of sickness; this starts with a mindset of not only caring for your chronic sickness, trying to maintain health, but moving beyond simple maintenance of health to new heights of striving for health improvement every day of our lives.

Our goal is to continue to thrive, not simply to survive! And our faith can play a mammoth role for good in this whole endeavor of health improvement.

HEALTH IS A MULTI-FACETED GEM

Your own health is an admixture of many, many factors. Some of these factors are completely out of your realm of personal influence. Factors such as heredity, the place and time of your birth, the health of your parents (especially your mother), prenatal care of your mother, childhood diseases, and others are all outside of your influential reach.

Other health factors however, are much more malleable, modifiable, and even changeable. You *do* have varying degrees of influence over these factors. These include: your diet, the amount and intensity of exercise you give your body, tobacco use, nutrition, sleep, relaxation, breathing, posture, adherence to safety principles, controlling stress levels, successful interpersonal relationships, and perhaps the most important of all, learning to use your personality as a wellness enhancement tool.

YOU ALWAYS HAVE SOME CONTROL

You may not have ever thought of it in this way before, but no matter what the condition or state of your health may be today, there is always some improvement you *can* make, usually almost immediately. You *can* change the state of your health at any time, in any place, in any circumstance! This is perhaps startling but true.

Think about this – no matter how dire your circumstances may be; you are still in charge of some measure of your health.

Even if you're sitting in a traffic jam, you can improve your posture while sitting in your car; even if you're flat on your back recuperating from surgery, you can improve your breathing; even if you're in the middle of washing the kitchen floor, you can change your thinking. You always have some control over some aspect of your health no matter how minute. Health improvement is always an option. You can make these changes yourself; you can act independently; you don't need active supervision or direction from anyone else, professional or otherwise.

HEALTH IMPROVEMENT FACTOR #ONE

The number one health improvement factor for persons in the second half of their life is to come to a full realization that change is not only possible... change is necessary. The systems of the body begin to change at the advent of the second half of your life in ways they have never changed before. Hormonal changes start slowly; eventually, however, these changes make their mark in ways that outwardly begin to make some part of your body thinner (most noticeable muscle mass) while other parts become thicker (most noticeably your waistline). These changes, and many others, call for action not only to help you stem the tide of the physical erosion that your natural maturation process is exerting upon you, but also as a means of solid health improvement.

Health improvement, even in the face of the physical changes of maturation, is always possible, desirable, and actually necessary for you to create optimal physical health. The questions:

"What can I do to improve my health today?"

"What is the most health-enhancing behavior I can perform right now?"

"What is/are the obstacles preventing me from improving my health today?"

...are all proactive and highly productive questions to ask. There is no time in life when health improvement is not possible, desirable, and necessary for optimal health. You can always improve your health, regardless of the physical, social, psychological, and/or spiritual condition.

BODY-MIND MEDICINE

Mature adults now have a new avenue to health improvement. Medical evidence is mounting each day that using mind-body techniques may not only improve the quality of life, but may actually alter the course of a developing disease. These studies are clearly showing that people can be active participants in their own health care; they *can* positively affect their health and bring it to an improved state. Mind-body principles cannot in themselves cure disease, but they can certainly reduce the severity and frequency of the physical symptoms that cause such distress.

Scientists are finding that there are many physiological connections between the central nervous system---the thinking and impulse-transmission mechanism of your body, and your immune system---the disease-fighting mechanism of your body. The precise mode of action of these connections remains somewhat mysterious, yet they do seem to exist and have been shown to play important roles in managing chronic disease. All these new findings have particular application to our lives as mature adults, because chronic disease is increasingly prevalent as we progress through the second half of life.

How do emotions like anger raise one's risk of heart attack, for example, especially in mature adults who are predisposed to coronary artery disease by heredity? How is it that close social ties serve as a significant protective mechanism against some diseases? These and other questions have particular application for maturing adults. All these questions and more are the subject of intense study. Someday we'll know more about how these mechanisms actually work. At that time we'll be better able to harness new techniques for more precise curative and healing purposes. Now, however, we must be content to recognize that these connections exist, and that they can be powerful tools for allowing maturing adults to live more vital and more functional lives, even in the face of chronic disease.

This chapter is designed to bring you one step closer to applying some well-known mind-body techniques in your everyday lives. These practices are not meant to supplant traditional medical practices; on the contrary, they are only meant to supplement the medical care you may already be receiving. You still need to seek the best medical care possible, yet physical care alone may be only a partial answer to finding relief. Mind-body techniques are powerful adjuncts to care which can alter your life and allow you to continuously improve the condition of your health in ways otherwise unavailable to us. This is why such health improvement techniques show unique promise for maturing adults who wish to thrive and not simply survive throughout their maturing years.

HARDINESS

Medical researchers Drs. George Solomon and John Morley studied the interactions between psychological factors and the functioning of the immune system in maturing adults. Their findings concluded that the immune system function is just as good as in persons half their age. Further, they found that improved immune system functioning is bolstered by the personality characteristics of what has become known as "hardiness" and is diminished by worry.

Personality "hardiness" includes four components:

1. **Challenge vs. Threat.** Being able to view life issues as challenges rather than as threats.

2. **Control vs. Helplessness.** Developing the attitude that one's own actions can influence events, rather than feeling helpless in the face of life events that one regards as overwhelming;

3. **Commitment vs. Giving-up.** Developing a mindset of fully investing your energies in whatever you are focused on, rather than simply doing as little as possible, or ignoring a situation altogether.

4. **Connectedness vs. Isolation.** Actively sharing yourself with others, rather than separating yourself from, or simply ignoring others.

It now seems all but indisputable that your attitudes and beliefs about wellness and well being have dramatic effects upon the actual physical functioning of your body. Your thinking and feelings impact your health dramatically. In general, positive thinking translates into a healthier immune system functioning, while negative thinking does just the opposite. The choice is actually yours to make: do you want to give your body functioning messages that say "Live" or "Die"?

GETTING TO THE HEART OF THE MATTER: GEORGE'S STORY

George, a 66-year old retiree from an electronics manufacturing plant, seemed to have a complaint about everything. Hardly an issue went by that he didn't feel compelled to comment upon in a most critical fashion. Each night of George's life he would watch the evening news and mumble under his breath about the terrible condition of the world. He punctuated his mumbling with outbursts like: *"Throw them all in jail!"* or *"Who could ever vote for that guy?"* or *"This country is headed for the trash heap!"* The stream of critical bile from his mouth seemed never-ending.

George's wife Margaret learned a long time ago that the best policy was simply to tune George out. This was particularly true when riding in the car with George. George constantly expounded on the stupidity of other drivers, and if any driver ever cut him off, inadvertently or not, he seemed to relish speeding up and either tailgating them or trying to pass them so he too could cut them off.

Going out socially in public was also a trial. At restaurants, George would demand service that was impossible for the waiters or waitresses to deliver. He routinely sent back entrées because of some imperfection he noticed, and would never wait more than ten minutes to be seated, all the while sighing and tapping his fingers or foot. George exhibited similar behavior in supermarkets, theaters, stores, and even in church.

George's exercise consisted of a round of golf "every now and then" in the warmer months; during the winter he took no regular exercise. George is a "meat and potatoes" man, preferring the diet he always enjoyed. Despite

Margaret's attempts to include more vegetables and fruits, George resisted angrily, asserting that he has a right to eat the way he wants, especially now that he's retired. George is 45 pounds overweight. His circle of friends remains the same from his working days. He sees his friends only infrequently, usually at their favorite restaurant for "a couple" and a big meal.

George had his first heart attack ten years ago, and has had another one since then. He was hospitalized both times, and went through the cardiac rehabilitation program the first time, but he seemed to lose his motivation for rehab on the second attack. George takes anti-hypertensive (high blood pressure) medication, cholesterol-lowering drugs, a tranquilizer, and a sleeping pill at night. He smokes a pack of cigarettes a day. He sees his doctor every six months for a checkup. Each time his doctor reasserts the points he made at George's last visit. George answers, *"Yeah, I know, Doc. I'll do better next time."* His weak resolutions never seem to become translated into any concrete action.

WELLNESS AND CANCER: BARBARA'S STORY

Even though Barbara knew she was walking erect, she felt emotionally unsteady and exceedingly vulnerable. She had just seen her doctor who reported to her the worst news possible: the lump Barbara had discovered in her left breast two weeks before was determined after a biopsy to be malignant. Barbara had cancer! Her doctor had outlined the treatment regimen, consisting first of surgery, either a breast removal or lumpectomy depending on the findings of the surgeon, most probably followed by chemotherapy and radiation lasting several months. The treatment would be arduous and dramatically life upsetting.

Barbara's emotions tossed and tugged at her as though she were being pounded and pummeled in an emotional washing machine. *"How could this be so?"* she wondered. *"This just isn't fair at all...at all...at all!"* she kept repeating. How she navigated herself home through her tears and her preoccupation remains a mystery. Once home, she kept asking herself what she had done to cause this terrible malady. How had she? Could she have done this to herself?

In chapter five of the book <u>Body-Mind Medicine</u>, Drs. Dennis Turk and Justin Nash pose this question: "Can your thoughts, emotions, or stress make you sick? And if so, can you 'think' yourself well?" The chapter goes on to outline the many, many studies that have searched for a "cancer-prone personality" and/or evidence that somehow we can "will" ourselves sick. The bottom line conclusions of the chapter indicate that no evidence exists to support a certain personality type or psychological behavioral pattern that predisposes a person to cancer of any type. Medical researchers have yet to substantiate that we can "think ourselves sick."

Yet there are behaviors that *can* assist us in our recuperation process. While the specific curative effects such supplementary rehabilitation techniques may have upon the progression of the sickness is, as of yet, undetermined (however tantalizing they may be from a medical standpoint), it is very clear that such techniques and practices do mightily support the patient as she goes through the medical treatment regimen that cancer generally requires.

Whereas we evidently cannot "will ourselves" either sick or well, we *can* bring about vital health improvements even under the direst circumstances of cancer treatment.

Health improvement is always possible.

What are these health improvement practices that have been shown to affect the stamina, the perseverance, and the "grit" of cancer patients, giving them some degree of control and forestalling helplessness and hopelessness?

1. **Support group participation.** Studies have clearly shown that involvement in a support group that is comfortable for you can substantially raise your overall level of life satisfaction while you are going through cancer treatment. It can affect the mortality rate over the long haul as well.

2. **A confidant**. Having a "buddy" with whom you can share not only your doctor visits but also your thoughts, fears, and joys exerts a tremendously positive effect upon sustaining treatment.

3. **Counseling**. The assistance of a professional health counselor can assist the patient in clarifying emotions and thinking so that decisions and actions can be most prudent.

4. **Hope and spiritual values**. Preliminary studies in this area suggest that spiritual and religious beliefs can positively influence the quality of a patient's life and enhance their immune system functions.

5. **Prayer and Meditation.** Prayer not only connects us with God and our own spiritual nature but also serves as a marvelous relaxation experience that "centers" us, placing us squarely on our true center of gravity, giving us emotional balance so necessary for healing.

WELLNESS AND PAIN: MARIA'S STORY

Maria, aged 76, suffers from chronic back pain. The doctors tell her that her back has become "unstable" due to a combination of 1) arthritic changes in the vertebrae of her back, 2) osteoporosis (degeneration of bone mass), and 3) slightly herniated vertebral disks (the soft tissue between vertebrae).

Maria suffers flare-ups of her arthritis periodically, and when she does, it sets off a chain of events leading to increasing pain. Maria deals with her arthritis flare-ups by taking to her bed for two or three days. While this does give her some relief, the prolonged bed rest makes her back muscles become shorter, tighter, stiffer, and weaker. This places them at greater risk for fatigue and muscle spasms causing Maria more pain. Then muscles surrounding the pained muscles begin to compensate for the restricted muscles and become overactive. This in turn causes them to become more prone to spasm and consequent pain. Spinal nerves become sensitized to the pain pattern and can become over-stimulated on a chronic basis, giving Maria the sensation of constant or "chronic" pain.

Maria's relief-seeking efforts for her chronic pain pattern involve a combination of medicinal remedies. She takes medications including: muscle relaxants, tranquilizers, pain pills, and an anti-depressant. She has had numerous cortisone injections in and around the tender areas of her back, and more recently (within the last two years) has had two separate surgeries that fused vertebrae in her spinal columns. Each of these efforts brings some measure of relief, but still the pain persists. Her doctors tell Maria she needs to learn how to deal better with her pain. She easily becomes more agitated, fearful, and angry – both at her doctors for not offering something more effective and permanent and at herself for thinking she has become weak. Over time Maria has become increasingly anxious, isolated, depressed, and preoccupied with her plight, as do many, many persons who suffer with chronic pain.

SELF-MANAGEMENT STRATEGIES

Maria can improve her health even in her rather bleak situation. Pain is felt subjectively; no two persons feel the same level of pain, even when they may be afflicted with exactly the same malady at the same intensity. Pain is personal and therefore it can respond, or at least be eased, by some behavioral techniques. As Drs. Dennis Turk and Justin Nash report in their chapter on "Chronic Pain: New Ways to Cope" in the book <u>Body-Mind Medicine</u>, *"The difficult truth for pain patients is that only their active participation in their treatment and their hard work are likely to help them improve and increase their functioning."* What is this "hard work" to which they refer?

1. **Relaxation.** The most common and useful technique for controlling pain is muscle relaxation. Recent research on pain control indicates a 38%

improvement for people suffering migraine headaches, and a 45% improvement for those suffering from tension headaches. This is impressive!

2. **Restructuring Your Thinking.** Whereas you can't think away your pain, it may be possible that changing the way you think about your pain may in itself alter your perceptions of your pain and actually give relief from it. By giving yourself thoughts that are mood-destabilizing, such as "This pain will never go away, I simply can't function with it," you may be doing one or all of three destructive things. First, such thinking erodes your sense of personal power and control. Second, such self-defeating thinking can actually cause increased muscle tension. Third, such thinking may alert your nervous system to widen the pain gate and increase your discomfort.

3. **Distraction.** Many chronic pain sufferers experience increasing isolation, either actually or psychologically, which only heightens their misery. Training your mind to think beyond the preoccupying pain and filling it with other thoughts can have a most positive effect upon your pain.

4. **Exercise.** Most chronic pain patients tend to avoid exercise because they fear more pain. Well-guided and constructive exercise, however, can do much to ward off the pain syndrome pattern that can emerge as it did with Maria.

WELLNESS AND DIABETES: BARRY'S STORY

Barry has suffered with diabetes for some 25 years now. At age 69 he is fully aware of the dangers and the problems associated with becoming lax with the treatment regimen that his doctors prescribed for him. His is Type II diabetes, the so-called adult-onset kind of diabetes. It was clearly in his family line; his father and an uncle both suffered from diabetes, as did his paternal grandmother and two of her sisters.

When he was first diagnosed, Barry's treatment consisted simply of a strict diabetic diet, along with regular exercise. After five years of these efforts, however, his condition worsened and oral medications were added. Oral medications increase insulin production in the pancreas and reduce the body's resistance to the hormone.

This combination sustained Barry for about another ten years. For the past ten years, however, Barry has been forced to take regular insulin injections on top of his exercise, diet, and oral medications. All was going fairly well until recently, when he became increasingly unable to control his sugar levels. His doctor began using the term "brittle" to describe this new phase of the diabetes. Barry became most concerned, for he was well acquainted with the consequences of uncontrolled sugar levels. What could he do?

STRESS AND DIABETES

It has been long recognized that stress can play a confounding role with diabetes. While stress alone does not seem to cause diabetes, it has been shown that stress can accelerate the onset of diabetes in persons already

Even Better After 50

susceptible to the disease through heredity. Stress can act on persons who are successfully managing their diabetes in two ways: First, stress can upset the person enough to cause them to forget their medications, to overeat, or to abandon their exercise program. Perhaps more indirectly, stress can, when experienced over time, cause an increase in the production of stress hormone (adrenaline). Such an increase is a normal reaction of the body, which is trying to bolster the energy stores of the individual so she or he can deal most appropriately with the new stressors in their life. This produces the effect (among others) of raising blood sugar levels. In normal people the added sugar is burned up as extra energy in the cells. In diabetics, however, this normal functioning is not possible, and their diabetic condition is aggravated as a result.

DIABETES AND DEPRESSION

Depression seems to afflict persons with Type II diabetes more than it does the general population. This combination is seen more strikingly as a person matures. Does this observation mean that diabetics are simply more susceptible to depression, or that the condition of diabetes is generally depressing – or both? Again, depression is not a cause of diabetes, or vice versa. Yet depression can heighten complications of diabetes. Prolonged depression is very stressful; it can cause stress-hormone releases just as other stressors can, which aggravates the diabetes. More sugar accumulates in the blood, which can move a formerly successful diabetes manager into an unhealthy condition of becoming "brittle" or uncontrolled. Here is where Barry found himself, and where extra measures need to be taken.

72

MIND-BODY TREATMENTS

Before the discovery of insulin in 1921, the most common remedy for diabetes was bed rest. This form of treatment was generally abandoned after 1921 in favor of insulin therapy alone; yet perhaps that was done prematurely. The latest medical studies indicate that stress management techniques can indeed help some people with their diabetes when used in conjunction with a medically prescribed and monitored treatment regimen. Patients who are taught relaxation techniques do show better diabetic control than other non-trained patients. Another study indicated that those diabetic patients who practiced relaxation techniques experienced fewer swings between high and low blood sugar levels.

INSIGHT QUESTIONS

1. To what degree do you see yourself on a continuous self-health improvement program?

2. What is the most health-enhancing behavior that you can perform right now?

3. How are you like George in "Getting to the Heart of the Matter?"

4. Have you ever participated in any of the health improvement practices listed in this chapter? Describe.

5. Have you ever used some of the pain self-management strategies that Maria used?

Part Two

The Art of Living Wisely

THE *MIND* DIMENSION OF OPTIMAL HEALTH

The second thrust of total wellness and well being is becoming wise. Being wise refers to one's attitudes about oneself and about one's place in the world. The term "mental wellness" probably comes closest to being wise. Being wise doesn't mean that a maturing adult has amassed mountains of knowledge. Rather, being wise means that the maturing adult has developed methods of approaching life that allow her or him to think clearly, accurately, and rationally about themselves and about others. Consequently such maturing adults act with wisdom rather than with ignorance or incompetence.

Wise living may be defined as our ability to use our mind in ways that bring us to ever-higher levels of positive and constructive living. At its core, wisdom is a way of thinking which determines the kind of world in which we live -- a world of loss, characterized by separation, grief, loss and fear; or one of growth, characterized by unity, cheer, abundance, and love. The world in which we live is much more a product of our own thinking processes than anything else. The kind of thinking that brings about healthy living is "wise" thinking.

WISDOM

- Wisdom is that power within us that enhances our ability to optimally use all the knowledge that we have "picked up" along our journey thus far.

- Wisdom bestows insight, good sense, sound judgment, and the ability to discern true inner qualities. Wisdom illuminates, enlightens, and permits solid singularity of purpose or direction.

- Wisdom confers spiritual intuition allowing us to penetrate into the true meaning and purpose manifested in our lives.

- Wisdom also permits us to discern God's presence in others, no matter how hidden that presence may seem.

- Wisdom vitalizes our thinking so that we can take full responsibility for what and how we think. In so doing, we can take on healthy living as our central lifestyle, and gain wellness in its fullest sense.

- Wisdom empowers us to clarify our thoughts and purify them in ways that beckon us to walk down lush garden paths of healthy living in body, mind, and spirit.

MENTAL HEALTH

Mental health involves so many things, so many personal characteristics, all of which have been shaped by: our genes, our family of origin, our education, our early experiences, our personal development in all life arenas, etc., etc. Mental health includes such factors as: our view of the world, general mood, risk-taking ability, personal organization, clarity of thinking, humor, openness, self-esteem, attitude toward learning, our emotions, and many others. As you can see, our overall mental wellness, or what we prefer to call "The Art of Living Wisely over the Lifespan," the second dimension of healthy living, is a complex amalgamation of the many ways we live our lives.

Like mental health, mastering the art of living wisely over the lifespan is not an either-or proposition, rather we gradually achieve higher and higher levels of wisdom about living our life as we mature; we gradually move closer and closer to creating a harmonious, integrated lifestyle; this is, of course, until we move into a new life stage where we are once again challenged to adjust our living so we can achieve a new balance of personal integration and settle in living wisely again. So how does a maturing adult master the art of living wisely?

Four characteristics of maturing adults who live wisely are:

Chapter Five: **Promoting Personal Health Power**. "Wise" maturing adults see themselves as persons who can generally make decisions on their own rather than being unduly influenced by outside forces. They value their self-control and self-discipline. They act with confidence, but also are respectful of the rights and the interests of others. They are *not* bull-headed.

Chapter Six: **Creating Healthy Relationships.** Perhaps because of their internal confidence, maturing adults who pursue a wise life enjoy people. They don't fear that they might be unfairly criticized, and if someone gets upset with them, they can handle the situation with appropriate social skill. They can share themselves and their lives, their joys, their trials, their delights, their hopes, and their sorrows, with others at appropriate times in appropriate ways.

Chapter Seven: **Learning the Art of Exceptional Living**. Wise mature adults proactively seek to inject change into their lives. They look forward to change to make things better. They recognize that all personal growth and development requires change, so they work to create a personal environment that makes room for and even encourages change, because they clearly understand that change means growth.

Chapter Eight: **Actualizing Wise and Positive Mental Attitudes**. Maturing adults living wisely view all the events in their lives, even the ones that may seem offensive or noxious on the surface, as further opportunities for personal growth and development. They develop a "challenge mentality" where they don't see threat in life situations; rather they see hope and a means for continued personal worth.

Chapter Five

Promoting Personal Health Power

Promoting Personal Health Power is the degree to which you can rely on your own resources to bring about the highest form of mental health by <u>making decisions</u> about your own life, rather than being unduly influenced by outside forces or persons.

Why is it that some maturing persons seem to rise to the challenges that life brings, while others seem to use their age as an excuse for exerting less energy into their lives? What forces, situations, characteristics, personal experiences, grace, or beliefs allow some "seasoning" adults to face the changes and chances that mature life brings, while others seem only to shrink from them?

Personal health power rests squarely on what we believe about ourselves and how we see ourselves at every stage.

79

Personal health power is not a behavioral competency but an attitudinal and self-perceptual competency. Yet our attitudes and our self-perception are the "mothers" of our behavior -- what we do! Personal power has everything to do with how we appraise and evaluate ourselves at this "seasoning" time of life, and how these appraisals of our abilities bring healthy and constructive change into our lives.

To what degree do you see yourself as sufficiently resourceful and appropriately capable of tackling the many modifications required for the life changes that maturing living brings so you can live a life of abundance?

CHANGE AND STRENGTH

Healthy mature life change requires strength, and strength is a God-given power that activates personal health power. All change, especially change in mature living, requires an attitude of "charting our own course," or self-empowerment, of being able to personally influence events and being resourceful.

Change demands self-control and self-discipline, two highly valued and central ingredients (virtues) of personal health power.

In our new, fast-paced world, change demands that we each act as our own quality centers of health promotion;

personal health power gives us the fuel so we can successfully address the many changes that challenge us in our life journey.

Personal health power is the first factor in "The Art of Living Wisely." The "Wise" dimension is also seen as the follow-through cluster of overall health enhancement, for it is here where the initiation or kick-off competencies of the "Well" dimension of health (the first four factors in the Well, Wise, & Whole model) are harnessed into action and eventually woven into the very fabric of your life, i.e., personal health power ensures that positive health change actually becomes a working reality in your life.

A POWER OFTEN MISUNDERSTOOD

Personal health power is often misunderstood. It's easy to think of personal health power in an absolute sense-that we either have personal health power or we don't. Actually, we all have some measure of personal health power; the question is to what degree have we tapped into our own personal health power, and in what ways are we choosing to use this power?

SELF-CONFIDENCE

Some maturing adults report feeling that their self-confidence is eroding. Increased self-confidence emerges as a by-product of acting with personal health power – making decisions. Self-confidence has two parts: 1) valuing yourself as an increasing integrating individual capable of using your strengths with clarity, and 2) finding the necessary resources to move you away from any of your weaknesses over to your strengths.

> *Self-confidence is not part of personal health power, rather self-confidence arises from personal health power as a consequence of its use.*

PERSONAL HEALTH POWER AND RELATIONSHIPS

In the book <u>Seasons of Strength,</u> authors Whitehead and Whitehead (married couple) give us a great insight into personal health power. They tell us that personal health power has everything to do with inner strength. They suggest that we not conceive of power as a packet of energy we have inside. Power is not the water in the reservoir; rather power is what's generated when the water is released and turns the turbines creating the dynamic force called power. Personal health power is the action of releasing the water (strength) that's already there in your internal reservoir.

To truly know your inner strengths, you need to come to an equal realization of your weaknesses and the changing patterns, opportunities, and challenges that maturing life offers every day. The change implicit in maturation challenges you to dig deeper into your potentials for personal health power. Change, then is both the challenge and the catalyst for personal health power development.

When we can recognize the weaknesses that lie in the shadows of our strengths, we reach a fuller, more integrated expression of your own personal health power. We're all weak in our own unique ways. Somewhere on our developmental path we are confronted with the inevitable truth that we can neither hide from, nor cover over our weaknesses; neither defend nor conquer them;

neither fix them nor rehabilitate them. Our weaknesses are our own; we must eventually come to own them. In doing so we find a new personal health power heretofore unrecognized and unappreciated; the power of inner peace and patient resolve.

PERSONAL HEALTH POWER ACTION PLAN

To bring this health enhancement competency into sharper focus in our lives, let's construct three personal health power personal goals. The following sentence stems are designed to help us construct our goals.

Directions: Complete the sentence in as concise and functional a statement as you can; these sentence completions become the foundations of personal goals.

1. *My primary learning from this book thus far is...*

   Goal No. 1: The one way that I can best bring this learning into my life at this time is to...

2. *If I could inject "personal health power" into my life on a truly consistent basis, my overall life in faith would...*

   Goal No. 2: The primary way I could be more consistent in bringing personal health power into my faith life is to...

3. The most important way that the information and personal insights that have emerged for me in this book thus far can help my work life become more fulfilling and personally meaningful is...

Goal No. 3: One way that I can help my life become more fulfilling and meaningful as a consequence of this book is...

STORIES

Here are short overviews of four maturing adults who for various reasons are (or have) stumbled into living lives with little personal health power. As you read these stories look for themes or patterns that are common to all four individuals described here.

ELVIRA'S STORY: HEALTH PASSIVITY

Elvira winced as she reached for her back with her left hand. Some weeks earlier Elvira fell in the hall. When she got up, she promptly fell again; she seemed increasingly unsteady on her feet. After a week in the hospital, Elvira emerged with a diagnosis of acute muscle strain. She went back home with the assistance of home health care and her doctor's strict orders for bed rest. This she dutifully followed, and followed, and followed. After four months of bed rest her doctor was flabbergasted that she had not yet started walking. He ordered her up and out of bed. Again, Elvira followed his advice but complained of pain. Medications and nerve stimulation apparatus were ordered, along with hot packs and massage. Again, Elvira followed her doctor's advice to the letter. Yet she did not get any better.

Elvira was not acting with personal health power. On the contrary, she left all her health decisions to her health care providers. She took little personal responsibility for her own recuperation; she lacked personal resourcefulness. Certainly we are to respect the recommendations of our care providers, yet Elvira needs to believe that she has some personal influence over her health. She needs to view herself as having some personal responsibility to activate her own internal fortitude and personal strengths in her recuperation. Elvira is not a passive dolt who only responds to the directives of her care providers; she is a proactive individual who has a mind and a will of her own.

Yet she has not realized the part she must play in her overall health; she is not acting with personal health power.

Her physical therapist told her that her back and neck muscles were "as hard as rocks" and that this was substantially adding to her pain. What could be the connection between her pain and her own thoughts? Interestingly, Elvira's background exposed that her mother was an exceptionally particular person. Everything had to be just right, indeed it had to be perfect or her mother would simply demand that Elvira do it all over again. Her mother was so particular that Elvira learned very early in life that she simply had to do as she was told. Any time that Elvira would try to exercise her own volition, she was criticized by her mom, sometimes benevolently and other times not; Elvira had to do things the "right" way, meaning her mother's way.

Elvira quickly learned to follow directions to the letter, and her mother generously complimented Elvira's obedience. Elvira grew up following directions, giving over to her mother at first, then to her teachers, and finally to anyone in authority (which included almost everyone). Elvira grew up with anemic personal power; her own thinking simply didn't matter.

As Elvira matured she transferred what she was taught by her mother, her teachers, etc., onto every situation she encountered. Consequently she became a very critical woman. If things weren't like her mother said they should be, even after her mother had long since died, Elvira would internally tighten. She would internally condemn other persons for not doing as they should. *"When will they ever learn?"* became a favorite internal question of hers.

Elvira became a roving critic; wherever she turned her gaze she would find something wrong. She came to expect that things were simply wrong most of the time; she anticipated that things were naturally wrong. This contorted perception allowed her to continue her critical ways, dutifully upholding the directives that her mother and others had given her so long ago. These directives live on to this day and continue to do damage by keeping Elvira's life in turmoil, and her neck and back muscles in constant and acute tension. Elvira exercises precious little personal health power; she is unhappy, in pain, and dramatically ill at ease in the world. Elvira has never learned to be her own person.

PAM'S STORY: SELF-AGENCY

Pam is a most faithful and generous woman. All through her life she has been faithful to the Church; she regularly attends Mass, receives the sacraments, dutifully brought up her five children in the faith, and supported the work of the Church in body, mind, and checkbook. It would be hard to find a more devoted Christian than Pam.

Now, at age 74, she sees herself in a predicament. She feels lost, unable to cope with the things that her husband formerly took care of. Her husband, Dick, has been dead for over a year. Dick was a formidable man – successful, strong, capable, and somewhat controlling. He was clearly the man of the house; Pam was rather comfortable in letting Dick run the finances of the household as well as many other tasks that needed doing. Dick was the primary decision maker of the two. It's not that Pam was submissive, on the contrary she was quite proactive and even opinionated when it came to the domestic matters of the house – the children, health care, food preparation, interior decorating, etc., etc. Yet Dick provided the strong power that could deal with the world; after all, he was a successful executive and was well acquainted, even savvy, with the ways of the world.

Pam could not act independently; rather she accommodated herself very comfortably to following Dick's lead. This posture was clearly not supporting her well now that Dick was gone. Pam started feeling not only mournful over Dick's death but somewhat angry as well. *"A strange emotion to feel,"* she mused. *"I was rarely angry at Dick when he was alive; why should I be now?"* Yet anger was most certainly mixed in with the avalanche of other emotions that she was feeling now that she was alone.

Her emotional discomfort grew to a point where one of her daughters suggested that she consult a counselor.

> *What emerged for Pam through counseling was that she had allowed her own sense of self to diminish over the course of her marriage.*

To some degree she forfeited her own self in the face of Dick's strong personality. Pam not only relied upon Dick, she had gradually, ever so slowly, yet without question, given up her own sense of self-agency.

SELF-AGENCY

Self-agency means that we have within ourselves the power to act on our own behalf, to exercise influence in ways by clearly expressing our own needs and wants. The notion of self-agency may sound selfish to a committed Christian; it may sound like a violation of humility and adaptability, or an act of vanity or self-centeredness. Yet, when and if we overlook our own needs, we can contort our humility into self-repression and our adaptability into self-forfeiture. Where is the line between these? This is part of our journey with Jesus as we grow spiritually.

Spiritual development does not mean self-repression or self-forfeiture, it does not mean submission or servitude. Spiritual development requires that we see ourselves as we actually are in the splendor of God's creation, that we conceive of ourselves in the richness and the abundance of our inheritance as children of God. Spiritual development requires that we act with self-agency.

*If we are to be as healthy as we can be,
we need to practice self-agency.*

TOM'S STORY: CREATING THE IMAGE

Tom is a very successful independent entrepreneur. At age 69 he still runs the family business, which he doubled, tripled, and quadrupled, over and over since his father left him the business 25 years ago. Indeed, Tom now has two of his sons working in the business as well. Tom is a well-known "pillar of the community"; he is a highly respected and sought-after "wisdom figure" in the town where he makes his home and runs his business.

Tom is acutely aware of the respect that is afforded to him and he makes every effort to uphold that trust. He sees himself as most privileged to have this recognition; it honors his reputation as a person and as a businessman. When Tom walks down the street, when he enters the barber shop, the drug store, the supermarket, really anywhere in town, he is aware that he carries on his shoulders not only the trust of the people in him as a business person, but also a personal awareness of himself as a successful and esteemed person of faith.

Tom clearly relishes this distinction; he can't imagine living a life without this recognition. He's careful to always "put his best foot forward." He buys tasteful, yet afordable clothes; he makes sure he drives an automobile that makes the right statement of stability; his home is gracious and comfortable, but not grand – nor does his home have any hint of being ostentatious. Everything about Tom says secure, conservative, tasteful, moderate, sensible, equitable, and above all beyond reproach. He never misses church services; he serves on the hospital board (but not the school board because then he'd have to make public his political preference and that might alienate some townspeople). He's very, very careful never to "ruffle any feathers," never to say a word which may even be misinterpreted as criticism of anyone, never have any air of self-aggrandizement, and never, never, never show anything distasteful or "off-color."

Lately, Tom's been feeling somewhat tired, fatigued, a bit slowed down, and even somewhat depressed. He's never felt this way before. He's even started to wonder whether anyone else has noticed these changes in him. He's tried to hide them all, but fears that he may not be accomplishing this goal to the best of his ability!

*Tom has been bothered more and more
by a sense of doubt in himself.*

He can't quite put his finger on the problem, but something seems to be "out of sync." He doesn't feel himself at all; he's even had thoughts of retiring, but he shrinks from that prospect. All he knows is his business and the town. *"Retiring would mean that I'd have to give up my esteemed position in the town,"* he muses. *"Retirement can't be the answer,"* thinks Tom, *"yet what can I do?"*

Tom has many blockers that prevent him from acting with self-agency. Even though he thinks of himself as a grandly independent person, in reality Tom is trapped by the servitude he renders to the image he has created in his community.

Tom is rigidly stuck in a behavioral "cow path" of his own making, a rut he seems unable to extricate himself from and which prevents him from expressing his own needs.

Sadly, Tom has lived his life for so long in this mode that he has long ago lost his own sense of self. He's out of touch with his own needs, having forfeited them to this artificial mask he's been wearing so long. Now he's confused about whom he actually is. Who is and where is the "real" Tom?

SIS'S STORY: SELF-CONFIDENCE

Sis was now 75 years old. Five years ago she moved from a city where she had lived for years to be near her daughter and her family. Other than her daughter, she didn't know a soul in the area. She knew this up front, but didn't think it would be an obstacle for her since she had started an Amway business some years before, and she thought she could simply move it to this new area. Actually she succeeded in this endeavor quite well. It was the other areas of her life that caused her such discontent.

Sis was the second of two daughters – the only children of her parents. Sis always thought of her older sister as a tower of strength. Her sister could do no wrong. Sis's sister was pretty, popular, smart; she had a great personality and a wonderful smile and laugh. All in all, Sis's sister completely outshone Sis in almost every conceivable area. Even though Sis knew that her parents loved her, she always thought of her older sister as the "preferred child." She wasn't bitter about this perception, rather she felt dispirited, personally unimportant, and just simply plain. Sis saw herself as the "plain Jane" sister.

Early in her life she developed an interest in art and reading. As a child and teen, Sis was always around the house but generally out of sight. She was "there" physically, but somehow "not there" socially; she seemed constantly absorbed in her books and her paints. Sis was shy, even what would be called "painfully shy." Rarely did she approach another person first. She always waited for them – for their entrance into her life or for their invitation for her to enter theirs.

> *Her shyness became an obstacle in her social development; it prevented her from reaching out to others.*

Gradually Sis's shyness congealed into some deficit in self-confidence. Sis began to truly believe that she simply "couldn't" do what others did, couldn't be what others seemed to be. Sis wondered, *"Why is it that others are so at ease, so confident, so sure of themselves? I'm always feeling so insecure, so sensitive, so fearful of saying the wrong thing, or maybe not saying the right thing."*

Finally Sis did meet a boy or rather the boy met Sis. He was the opposite of her. He seemed strong, confident, and self-assured; everything that she lacked he seemed to have in abundance. She felt secure with him, she felt strong; she seemed to draw strength from him. They married, and she soon found that he seemed more interested in his path to success than in her. Once again, Sis felt diminished, living in the shadow of a much stronger person. But that was all right with her, because by the time there were two little ones in the house, Sis was a mother. Sis loved motherhood and adored the two "little people" who depended on her. She felt more assured during this time of life than perhaps any other.

Her husband was still away on business much of the time, yet Sis learned to live without him at home. In a way it was almost easier for her when he was away; she could "command" her own life rather than having to forfeit herself to his. It wasn't that he was in any way abusive, it's just that he was so self-absorbed in his own world, which, by the intense power of his own self-interests, pushed Sis's needs and wants to the 'back burner."

> *Sis was simply overpowered by her husband's dominant personality.*

This emotional imbalance between Sis and her husband emerged into a relationship symbiosis that continued until the two children went off to college. Once they did, Sis was alone. Her primary purpose in life had just walked out the door. What was she to do?

Somehow she found her own business. She could run it from her home and could use it as her primary means of connection with others. She gradually built up a clientele to whom she gave the most personalized and unselfish service possible. Sis's customers became her new source of confidence; in a sense she lived through them, she could become someone she liked, someone whom others liked as well. Sis mourned her husband's death from a sudden heart attack, but her life changed very little. She simply invested more of herself in her business and her customers, who of course were more than customers to her. Sis's confidence in herself was not hers; it came to her through her customers. We each find our own confidence – where does yours come from?

INSIGHT QUESTIONS

1. What is your overall level of 'personal health power?'

2. Where are you with your own self-confidence?

3. What is the central message of Elvira's story?

4. Do you have 'self-agency?' Describe.

5. Can you see the direct connection between and among:

   a. The four stories described in the chapter.

   b. Personal health power.

   c. Your overall mental health? Describe.

Chapter Six

Creating Healthy Relationships

*Creating Healthy Relationships is the
degree to which you can develop
relationships of sharing for the purpose
of accurately communicating yourself,
and thereby focusing your energy toward
valued goals of personal growth and
optimal living.*

The sixth competency area in our Even Better After 50 program for creating "optimal health" in the maturing adult years is 'Creating Wise Relationships.' Here is the heart of the wisdom section of health. There is no question that wise living includes developing and maintaining fulfilling and meaningful interpersonal relationships on various levels of social contact.

Even Better After 50

THE UNIVERSAL PULL TOWARD RELATIONSHIP

Every listing of the characteristics that produce strong mental health always includes the ability to make and keep friends... the ability to develop, nurture, and maintain intimate relationships. Yet why is relationship building so important? Why are we so compelled to interact with our fellows? It turns out that relationship building is imprinted in us.

1. **Physical level.** We have a long heritage of developing relationships. In our primitive state, mankind depended upon cooperation with his or her companions for survival in the forest. An individual person was decidedly vulnerable in the wild. When people clustered together, when they learned to cooperate through communal hunting, defense, gathering food, and the like, their chances for survival rose dramatically.

2. **Social level.** With increasing complexity, groups of humans formed tribes and/or communities. Such cooperation required relationship development and an ongoing energy to sustain the cohesion of the group. In a very real sense, the better the tribe became at relationship building, the greater their chances for ultimate success, expanded property, wealth development, and power. Relationship building now went beyond survival and included social and cultural development.

3. **Psychological level.** Relationship building gives us something more basic than even our survival needs; it gives us a sense of ourselves, a sense of who we are. Interpersonal relationships provide us

with information about ourselves that could be gathered nowhere else.

We learn who we are through our relationships.

It is in encounters with others that we come to understand more completely what is actually on our minds. We are always in a process of growth, of individuation, of becoming all that we can become, certainly with God's grace.   On a psychological level this means developing a clearer awareness of who we are. The better we can express what we are thinking and what we are feeling, the more accurately we can come to know the uniqueness of this wonderful personality given to us by God.

4. **Spiritual level**. Relationship building is the story of our ongoing dialogue with God. Human encounter prepares us for encounters with God. In a very real sense, we come in contact with the divine as a consequence of our interactions with others. As we deepen our relationships with others, we quite naturally grow closer and closer to the core of our personality... the place where we find God within. Here is where we discover spiritual intimacy – that condition where we come to know and can share the unique truth, beauty, and goodness with which God has blessed us.

WE NEED RELATIONSHIPS

We crave relationship. When we engage others even on the most superficial levels we actually feel better, we feel like we belong, we feel greater security and greater safety. The renowned psychologist, Abraham Maslow, gave us a hierarchy of personal needs; he claimed that we organize our lives to satisfy these five broad areas of need. They are: 1. Physical needs: food, clothing, shelter, etc., 2. Safety and security needs: protection from threat, 3. Belonging needs: the need to be part of a group, 4. Self-esteem needs: the need to experience the affirmation of others, and 5. Self-actualization needs: the process of becoming all we can be. Relationship building fosters life satisfaction on all five levels of human need. No wonder we are compelled to form relationships; without them we would become sick and die.

RELATIONSHIPS AND SPIRITUALITY

Relationships create closeness between two people. This closeness can be viewed as a step toward experiencing the goodness inherent in each partner and thus brings each closer to the other spiritually.

It is through relationships that we encounter God.

God is love and it is only in relationship that we can love. We are "in love" when we are in relationship. Naturally the quality of the relationship determines the degree of spirit stimulation generated from it, but whatever the quality, we always have the option of viewing each of our relationships through the eyes of Jesus.

RELATIONSHIPS AND MATURE LIVING

The maturing years are times of tremendous growth as we are asked to continuously deal with the challenges, changes, and adaptations that accompany the maturation process; it's a time of shifting needs, of transferring energies, of adjusting priorities. These changes do not happen in a vacuum but in the context of a social unit -- a couple, a family, a social circle of friends, a community, a work group. With all changes on an internal level, adjustments must be made in our relationships as well. Couples need to adjust to retirement, families need to adjust to sickness, friends need to adjust to relocations and loss due to deaths, communities need to welcome new members, and work groups need to adjust to the varied demands with decreasing person-power. Relationship changes are universal; yet there are some commonalities or relationship competencies that help us better understand these needed changes.

THE SIX COMPETENCIES OF QUALITY RELATIONSHIPS

There are six "relationship competencies" that characterize quality relationships; the more these six competencies are practiced in any relationship, the higher the quality of the relationship, and the more fulfilling the relationship for both partners, regardless of the type of the relationship (see Loving for a Lifetime). Not all relationships require high levels of all six, but each of the six must be present in all relationships to some degree for relationship efficiency and effectiveness to emerge.

1. **Mutuality vs. Selfishness**. The human relationship condition created when each partner in a relationship of any kind believes she or he is

involved in a human connection of shared purpose, and where each partner's overall needs are valued equally, creating a union of interdependence. The opposite or threat to mutuality is selfishness or submissiveness. When mutuality is not present, an unhealthy dominant/submissive relationship often emerges. The dominant partner becomes increasingly self-centered, while the submissive partner becomes increasingly suppressed. In such a situation, one partner's needs and wants take precedence over the other partner's, thus weakening the relationship.

2. **Respect vs. Resentfulness**. The human relationship condition created when each partner in a relationship sees the interior uniqueness of the other. Each partner's personal specialness is honored by the other partner as a part of the gift of that person. The primary threat to respect is contempt, or resentfulness. When respect is violated, there emerges an internal sense of holding the other partner in the relationship somehow responsible for the ill feeling of the first partner. Resentfulness stifles and even poisons the relationship – whatever type of relationship this may be: a neighbor, a co-worker, a friend, a spouse, or whatever.

3. **Communication vs. Criticism.** The human relationship thinking condition created when each partner in a relationship uses clear and understandable language to connect with the other, so information can be exchanged with efficiency and inevitable differences can be worked

out. The opposite or primary threat to communication is criticism, when relationship partners move into an "attack" mode with one another. Each partner constantly scans the other for imperfections in an attempt to discredit the partner and demonstrate who is "right" in the relationship.

4. **Intimacy vs. Withdrawal**. The human relationship feeling condition created by an emotional bond of attachment, and some level of affection, which at times requires personal sacrifice. The opposite or threat to connection is withdrawal. Connection is about coming together at ever deepening levels, sharing one's inner self. Withdrawal happens in many ways, most of which revolve around fear: fear of closeness, fear of losing control, fear of self-depreciation.

5. **Trust vs. Doubt.** The human relationship deciding condition created when each partner in a relationship can rely upon the other. The opposite or threat to trust is doubt. Suspicion or fear that one is being betrayed or neglected can lead to the condition of doubt as a pervasive condition of the relationship. Sharing occurs less and less when trust is low.

6. **Commitment vs. Indifference.** The human relationship action condition created when each partner in a relationship exercises varying levels of personal staying power, patience, and steadfastness to one another. The opposite or threat to perseverance is avoidance. Being

avoidant means that the partner diverts, shies away from, or otherwise dismisses the central issues that the other partner is trying to sustain.

All human relationships include one or more of these six to a greater or lesser degree. As we move up Maslow's hierarchy of needs we include more of these six. As the nature of the relationship deepens, we see that these six relationship competencies are brought into play at higher and higher levels. On the first level of need, that of "survival," we require only the third relationship characteristic, that of communication. For example, when you go into the supermarket and order smoked turkey at the deli counter, the only relationship competency we absolutely need is communication. On the second level of safety and security, we need to add the relationships competencies of No. 5, trust, and No. 2, respect, when interacting with a police officer, for example. On the third need level of belonging, we need to add the relationship competency of No. 4, closeness. On the fourth level of need, "self-esteem," we require more from the relationships with persons closer to us, and we need to add the competency of No. 1, mutuality. Finally, for relationships developed on the fifth level of need, the spiritual level, which include spouse and confidants, we need to add the competency of No. 6, commitment, into the mix.

INTIMACY AND MATURE ADULTS

More than ever, maturing adults need to maintain and even improve their relationship skill levels to high degrees so they can meet the cascade of changes they encounter in an ever-shifting lifestyle. The closer the relationship, the deeper and broader we're called to rely upon the six relationship competencies.   The notion of a closer relationship is one where there is sharing of inner self. The more sharing... the deeper the sharing, the more intimate the relationship.   Increased intimacy (sharing) calls for ever-broader relationship competencies at ever-deeper levels.

Intimacy is characterized by truth telling, revealing to the other what is truly on one's mind. This element of self-disclosure involves a sharing of some of the innermost perceptions, thoughts, feelings, and decisions currently experienced by the person.

Intimacy is our inner yearning to be known, understood, and confirmed as a person on our own terms.

Intimacy is a basic motivational force for us. As change occurs in our lives at the quickening pace that it does, our need for a more or less continuous reaffirmation is self-evident.

There is mounting evidence that intimacy builds physical and psychological wellness.   When this concept is extended to spiritual intimacy, where two people can share of themselves on deep spiritual levels, giving testimony of the ways God is working in their lives, we see that such sharing enhances total health in the process. Intimacy seems to charge the total well being of a person, bringing with it a heightened sense of life satisfaction and a consequent stimulation of thriving, rather than simply surviving.

THE MANY KINDS OF RELATIONSHIPS

Intimacy manifests itself in many relationships. Marital relationships certainly need high levels of intimacy. Next we could include relationships with a confidant, someone with whom one can fully share issues such as failures, triumphs, doubts, delights, fears as well as fantasies, really anything. A confidant would be a good friend, a spiritual director, a professional counselor, a physician, priest, minister, etc.

Families generally offer numbers of relationships; in addition to the marital relationship we find lots of others: children, siblings, in-laws, cousins, aunts, uncles, nieces, nephews, grandchildren, etc. These provide opportunities for social interchange with varying degrees of intimacy.

The next category of intimacy is friendships. These offer perhaps the broadest array of sharing opportunities. We have distant friends, "fair weather friends," good friends, better friends, best friends, and "fast" friends.

Deepening relationships shield us from some of the most insidious dangers, changes, and challenges of maturing adult living: isolation, alienation, separation, loneliness, loss, cynicism, and depression.

Relationships are the wellspring of our wellness; they also offer us new wisdom.

But finally, and most importantly for us as people of faith, relationship building on this material level serves as the basis and foundation for building our relationship with God. It is only in relationship with others that we can experience the reality of God in our lives and God in the world.

Here are several stories that portray various types of relationships. Look for the relationship commonalities in these. Also look for how your relationship(s) stacks-up to these.

JANE AND TOM CUMMINS

Jane and Tom Cummins have been married for 43 years. Tom is retired from a large corporation where he worked for over 25 years. The Cummins' three children are all married; one lives in the same metropolitan area as the Cummins, the other two in rather distant cities. They have five grandchildren (so far).

Since Tom retired two years ago, the quality of the relationship seems to have eroded a bit. Jane particularly doesn't feel the same sense of togetherness that she formerly did; they each seem to be going their separate ways. The relationship doesn't provide a mindset of "coupleness," the two of us together creating a distinct "WE." The bond that formerly seemed so tight is loosening; the companionship level has been negatively affected, as has the sense of partnership that was formerly there. In Jane's eyes, Tom has become somewhat self-centered and self-absorbed; it's only his needs that seem to count. This is a change for the marriage, and one that has robbed it of some of its quality.

Formerly attentive and quite considerate, Tom has become somewhat neglectful, insensitive to Jane's needs. Personal idiosyncrasies that used to be an item of humor now seem to catch Tom's attention in a negative way.

Some days Jane feels like the maid rather than an honored spouse; she doesn't feel the specialness in Tom's eyes of years past. Tom wants her "there" with him at all times. When Jane tries to arrange social ties with friends, Tom seems to sneer.

Communication was never one of Tom's strong suits, but since his retirement, whatever sharing on a positive and intimate level he used to do has been leached out of the relationship. Daily interactions between Tom and Jane seem to devolve into misunderstandings more often. Tom's normal reaction after an altercation is to storm out of the house without a word. The best they can do together is watch television; even then, however, Tom lobs criticisms at the news announcer. The enjoyment of just sharing that was formerly present has eroded from their relationship.

Tom seems distant and over-engaged in his own thoughts. The everyday displays of affection that Jane had grown to expect from him are now gone. His passion has waned tremendously; the warmth of the relationship has cooled considerably. There seems little emotional refreshment from their interactions. In so many ways, Tom has withdrawn from the intimate sharing that they had in the past.

Jane still has deep feelings for Tom, yet his emotional resignation has leached a layer of trust from Jane's world. It's not that she doesn't trust Tom, for his fidelity is unquestioned; it's just that Jane can't seem to trust him with her feelings as she once did. He either doesn't respond or he takes parts of what she shares with him and turns it into a negative when that wasn't her intent at all.

Jane wants to be supportive of Tom; she senses that he is going through a painful time of transition. In former years he was mightily invested in his work; since his retirement, however, he's found nothing that could replace the intensity of interest that he had with his work. He misses his work, his co-workers, and his sense of involvement. Yet even with this insightful understanding, Jane feels the bonds of the relationship have loosened. The deep friendship that they formerly shared has eroded; spending time together seems to have become a chore rather than a pleasure.

THE OLYMPIA DINER

Hank could already smell the bacon and eggs cooking as he walked in the front door of the diner down the street from his apartment. He had come to the Olympia Diner for years, and practically owned the second stool from the end of the counter, where he placed himself every morning. Like clockwork Hank appeared at the diner door at precisely 6:45 every morning, and like clockwork Susan was pouring his morning coffee before Hank could rest his elbows on the counter. No words were spoken; the only signal that Hank wanted his "usual" was the slightest nod of his head as his eyes met Susan's. Within minutes Hank's eggs, toast, bacon, and hash browns were there in front of him, prepared to his exact, yet unspoken specifications.

The ease with which this interchange occurred seemed like a well-choreographed dance routine. The sense of sharing created by this simple task was a pleasure both Susan and Hank enjoyed with equal satisfaction. The common purpose of breakfast was the currency for an emergent sense of togetherness, a warm companionship, and a collaborative partnership that bonded these two in a casual yet profound way. They each knew their respective parts to play, parts which buffered them from an alienation that a harsh world sometimes presents. The interchange was a daily fortification of safety and security, a message that all was well today.

There was genuine humility in the encounter. The diner provided a place where both Hank and Susan could be their true selves: no baggage, no pretense, no masks, just simple respect and an honoring of each person. Each partner's individual good was served with the distinction of Sunday morning worship. Hank's thoughts of Susan gave him pause to appreciate the day, be grateful for his own presence, and once again count his uniqueness. Likewise Susan received this affirmation and savored the unspoken appreciation with each movement of the ritual.

While little was said, much was communicated. A hidden empathy, as strong as the coffee, expressed itself with an aroma that spoke of human genuineness. During this "sacred" time every morning each of them knew the other without falter; each step was captured and measured, each movement noted and approved, each look recognized and taken in. Each communicated the uniqueness of their understanding of the other, each with their flaws that had become friends over the years. With few words they spoke an encyclopedia of information that fortified an understanding and a blessing that opened the day like a prayer.

With no passion, each showed devotion, a sharing of souls as if each was looking into an emotional mirror.

Compliments were slung back and forth in silence like hash browns sizzling in thin air. Hank and Susan both gave the other a caring support of their inner core that left each of them with the flow of "rightness." The only union that would ever occur between them happened right there at the counter in the same way each and every morning.

While neither ever asked the other for more than what could be transferred over that diner counter, each knew without question that there existed in each other's hearts a trust baked as perfect as a morning biscuit. Honesty mirrored honesty when their eyes met as Hank rose from his stool, slung his leg away from the counter, and fixed a toothpick between his teeth. This rhythmic motion gave epilogue to the mingling of souls that transpired there the same time each morning.

Each was left with feeling of constancy, knowing that another installment had just been paid on the reliability of life. The anxiety that can visit them both had been at bay for at least another day. Now each could continue on in safety and stability, and meet the additions and subtractions of the day, continuing in confidence that tomorrow the dance would again be danced, the play would again be performed. And this was good.

PERFECT FRIENDS

Sharon and Helena were widows, each having lost husbands within six months of the other. These events seemed but extensions of the parallels that Sharon and Helena shared in their lives for so long.

Both were born just months apart into families living on the same block. Each was the third of five children. Both went to the same parochial school and shared the same teachers from grade one through eight. You see their names began with letters but two spaces apart in the alphabet, and since St. John's Grammar School was methodically alphabetical, this offered almost ironclad insurance that Sharon and Helena would not only be in the same class but would find a way of sitting right next to each other.

The girls graduated from the same high school and both married local boys just as they returned from war. They moved to the same suburb and began the process of duplicating over and over not only the patterns of their own lives, but those of their children as well. In almost every arena of family and human activity, Sharon and Helena mirrored each other – not in any competitive way, but with a complementarity that seemed as natural as a sunny October day.

Now they shared a sense of safety in the bitterness of their respective losses. Their tragedies welded the bond they shared into a mutual "WE" of peace and security. They enjoyed a special mindset of "us" and an unspoken belief that their relationship brought them peace and security. They had common purpose of companionship, as they always had; their togetherness was never questioned, their "specialness" was evident. They were partners.

Sharon honored Helena and vice versa. In their honesty, the relationship grew strong, with each of them believing the other to be her most respected ally. The familiarity between them was palpable, their devotion and attachment gave homage to the other. Each taught the other that support was expected and always counted upon. Each affirmed the other, complemented the other, and counted on the other without question. They were more than friends; they were confidantes.

They developed an understanding of each other that was dazzling. They communicated through a knowing heart as much as by words, but words were never lacking. In their relationship there existed full communication... mechanisms of interaction and expression that were not completely known even to them. Each friend simply "knew" the other so well that their verbal interchanges were more confirmations of ideas already communicated without words, rather than exchanges of new information.

Sharon and Helena were connected with little if any reservation. What belonged to one also belonged to the other. Their affection and devotion to one another flowed like rivers through ancient canyons. They understood each other, they affirmed and even celebrated each other with feelings of filial love both pure and beautiful. They mattered to each other like sturdy bookends. Their sharing touched every area of their lives; it permeated them. Yet the relationship seemed keenly respectful of the need for personal independence.

Over the years, as the changes ebbed and flowed in their lives, they served as each other's mechanism for adaptability. Facilitating, fostering, and even brokering change in each other's lives, they served as change catalysts for each other. Mentors and teachers, mirrors for one another, they flourished as two healthy trees grow full and strong in a meadow which allows room for each to spread their limbs and leaf out fully. They cross-pollinated each other with the finest, most fertile growth stimulators.

All of this added up to an unparalleled permanence in the relationship. They sustained each other, they balanced one another, and they gave stability to each other. They joined their minds and souls for life, living life in tandem, yet unconfined. The bonds they developed never aged into glue sticking them together against their will; rather their bonds gave them steadiness and relational confidence which bred perseverance, tenacity, and stamina.

INSIGHT QUESTIONS

1. How high is your need for relationship? Describe.

2. Which is your strongest relationship competency (of the six) in your marriage (primary) relationship? Weakest?

3. What do you see as the connections between relationships and wellness? Describe.

4. Are relationships needed more in the younger years or in the maturing years? Describe.

5. Which of the stories of different kinds of relationships do you like the best? Why?

Chapter Seven

Learning the Wise Art of Exceptional Living

Learning the Wise Art of Exceptional Living is the degree to which you proactively seek to inject change into your life.

Living well is an art; it implies that persons accurately perceives their own surroundings and personal resources, is in charge of their thinking, and can make appropriate choices for a life of fulfillment, satisfaction, and enjoyment. At the center of living exceptionally, especially in one's maturing years, is the mega-skill of remaining open to change. This ability, remaining open to change, is *the* essential point of this seventh "optimal health" competency.

How and why is it that some maturing adults revel in change, embracing it with gusto and glee? They seem to capture all that is new, they are vitally interested in the world, they relate with others freely, they find stimulating endeavors that delight their souls; in short, they are fully alive and maximally healthy. Yet we find other maturing individuals who seem quite the opposite - they seem to fight life itself. They resist changes of any kind; they seem to want the world as it was yesterday. They may show their reluctance in many ways: irritability, frustration, depression, withdrawal, avoidance, denial, etc., etc. These maturing adults are slowly dying, they are not healthy, they are not living full lives, they refuse to change... and they generally become very sad!

In 1970, Alvin Toffler's book <u>Future Shock</u> appeared. It made the forceful case that our culture was moving so fast that those who have not mastered the skills of change were suffering. He called his condition of change resistance "future shock." He wrote, *"It became clear that future shock is no longer a distantly potential danger, but a real sickness from which increasingly large numbers already suffer. This psychobiological condition can be described in medical and psychiatric terms. It is the disease of change."* (Page 2)

Toffler identified maturing adults as most vulnerable to future shock because their formative years were in a time when the pace of change was much slower than today; consequently they were not forced to learn the skills of change and are not able to pace themselves to the tremendous *"...roaring current of change, a current so powerful today that it overturns institutions, shifts our values, and shrivels our roots."* (Page 1)

Adult development and maturation is about change!

CHANGE IS FUNDAMENTAL

Remember your earliest memory: what was occurring? You created a memory of this event because some core belief changed within you; in some dramatic way you came to some startling realization on that occasion. Why else would it remain imprinted on your memory after these many years if you somehow hadn't changed at that particular time? Your life shifted then, in some way you changed; you added a new belief, shifted your perception, injected new thoughts into your life, experienced very stimulating feelings, made a life-shifting decision, or took some robust action. In some significant way, you changed your life, or your life was changed for you, on that day. Also on that day, you matured.

When you were a baby, and for the first time got up off your all-fours and took your first steps, on that day you matured; the day you went off to school for the first time, you matured; when you went on your first date, when you took your first job, when you left your family of origin, over and over, and on and on, you matured. Maturation is good, it is God's plan, and it is why God placed you here on this earth.

You can't escape maturation; certainly you wouldn't want to, for you would miss all the "stuff" of life. Yet somehow when the maturation process proceeds into the middle and later stages of living, we sometimes want to squirm out of maturation, at the very least we want to slow it down, or be more selective about it. We start digging our figurative heels into the dirt of the present day and begin refusing the future, refusing the developmental imperative that God has laid out for us. On the day when we start turning our back on change, we close down to growth, and we start to die to ourselves.

Maturation works to our advantage spiritually, provided that we remain open to change, and not try (consciously or not) to tenaciously hold onto our former ways of the thinking and feeling.

> *Change means that we shed some of what was before and replace it, not with more complexity, more "stuff" of the world, but replace it with internal growth.*

As we mature we increase in wisdom, in charity, in faith, in hope, in trust; at times we are forced to become more dependent. Especially at times of loss, our true spiritual Self grows like never before.

Our world is a world of change. Generally we find change fascinating, yet, when change starts chipping away at who we have defined ourselves to be, the fascination we derive from change can turn to fear. Aging affects our lives at every level, because aging brings great change. This change occurs physically, mentally, emotionally, psychologically, and spiritually. We can be blind to our fear of change. We can clearly see the need for change in others, yet we can easily overlook and even repress the need for change in ourselves. *"If she would only groom herself a bit better she would be so much more appealing!*

If he weren't so grumpy all the time I would talk to him more. Why doesn't she _____ more?" (Fill in the blank). Statements like these and many others so strikingly point up the ease and clarity of our perception when viewing others. If we could only be so observant and casual about spying our own shortcomings!

So often it's not until we are pushed to the proverbial edge that we reluctantly make the behavior changes that perhaps could have been made more efficiently some time before. How many smokers didn't quit until their doctors had already discovered health damages from smoking? Or how many retirees now wish they had saved and invested wisely much earlier? How many divorces could have been avoided if one or both partners had been able to move to forgiveness sooner, or away from criticism earlier? Indeed, why is it that marriage counselors are doing a booming business while marriage enrichment seminars are notoriously sparse in attendance?

Most people don't change until they are pushed by compelling challenges that would exact enormous pain of some kind if changes were not made. Even though change is the natural order of things on this plane, change is certainly not revered as the premier agent of growth and health enhancement that it is. Douglas Smith wrote about this in his book Taking Charge of Change... *"Threatening circumstances and challenges compel both performance and change much more effectively than mere opportunities and good intentions."* (Page 6)

CHANGE AS A HEALTH ENHANCER

We find it difficult to recognize change as the health enhancer it is. We tend to ignore or deny change rather than embrace change as our friend. Yet change is the wellspring for our growth and development. Every day is supposed to bring something new. Every day, then, is about change. Yet, do we see these everyday opportunities for change? Do we regularly seek changes that would improve our health and personal development? Do we undertake the "work" necessary so we can develop a mindset that stimulates change in us?

Uncertainty is the No. 1 cause of stress in our lives, and yet the opposite, not enough change, can---paradoxically--- also create stress. In the lives of many mature adults it is the latter, not enough change, not enough stimulation that causes more stress. We find ourselves too quickly falling into what has been called the "cow path" mode of living, when today is lived out very much like yesterday and we don't allow change to enter into our lives. We may become fearful of change, fearful of what tomorrow may bring, to such a degree that we figuratively walk the same course that we did yesterday, psychologically playing the game that "if it worked yesterday, it's sure to work today." The trouble with living a "cow path" lifestyle is that sooner rather than later we begin experiencing stress reactions. We can become irritable, bored, depressed, lethargic, unresponsive, self-absorbed, and simply out of sorts.

When we refuse to make our own changes, it pretty much guarantees that circumstances will push us to change in ways that we probably won't like.

TOLERANCE FOR AMBIGUITY

Change requires that you recognize your inner potentials and capacities, as well as learn how to place trust in yourself. With all the adjustments and all the modifications that are asked of us as we mature, it's common that some self-doubt invades our psychological space from time to time.

Change is hard because it always demands that we forfeit something, that we lose something. Loss may be the primary driving force behind positive, constructive change. At every life stage we must face losses, and as a consequence of these losses we are compelled to change. When our last child leaves home to strike out on his or her own, we experience loss; when sickness strikes, we experience loss; and when we retire from our work, we experience loss. This list expands as we mature. Each of these losses mandates change; the change can be external, as in the case of sickness, where we lose the ability to go to work or play, or it may be internal, where we are forced to shift our attitudes about being the oldest generation when our parents die. These changes are sustaining; they allow life to go on and growth to continue. Without change life withers.

Any and all personal successes begin with change. Success doesn't come from remaining the same; success requires change. Think of a success that you have experienced, a public success like buying a new home, or a private success like giving up smoking, losing weight, or learning to get along with someone who had formerly unnerved you. Any of these successes require change, and changes usually involve loss.

Jesus asked us to change; he asked us for conversion and redemption, to turn around our old ways and take on new ways. Jesus expects us to be different today than we were yesterday; he expects us to be better people, to love more, to have deeper faith, and to know him better. All this requires change. Our prayer is a request for change, even when we pray for our health to remain stable, or our marriage to stay strong, or our children to do well in this world; whatever we ask for is really a request for change. Jesus asks that we see things in a new way, that we see them in the light of Jesus, in the hope of God.

Letting Go for Growth

Remember those Tarzan movies? Tarzan swings through the jungle from vine to vine. With little effort he seems to grab one vine, swing through the air, and miraculously find another vine which he grabs and swings, and so on! How smooth and graceful Tarzan's movements seem to be; how quickly he can move through the jungle on his journey usually saving Jane or his chimp, Chita.

What would happen if Tarzan didn't let go of the first vine before grasping for the second? Can't you just see him hanging with one hand still grasping for the second vine! What would happen to his forward motion? How graceful and effortless would he appear then?

The lesson is simple; yet how many times in our lives are we "stuck," unlike Tarzan, holding on to old attitudes, old perspectives, and old thoughts? Such an antiquated inner life causes only negative feelings, tired decisions, and the kinds of action that keep us in the same old rut. This is certainly not a prescription for creative senior living!

Letting go is a challenge to a whole new way of living. Senior life may confront us with problems which require us to let go of the old and come up with creative ways of living from a new vantage point. Senior life may ask us to let go physically, to let go of what we once were. It may ask us to let go mentally so that we don't simply build our present lives around yesterday's memories, or live with long held resentments. Sometimes we may even have to cleanse our minds.

Living creatively at any age, but particularly in the senior years, calls us to let go emotionally. We must learn to let go of things that we once treasured, something or someone that once stood at the center of our lives. Finally, we need at times to let go spiritually. With the onset of issues and incidents that are simply bigger than our personal resources, we need to appeal ever more deeply to God's power. We need to get ourselves out of the way and let God enter in! Spiritually we are not islands; rather we are bridges enabling us to journey to a whole new world where we can rely upon One stronger than ourselves.

Letting go is not easy stuff. Our American culture values a rugged individualism and accents personal achievement; we are taught from a very young age to seek responsibility to "do it yourself" if you want it "done right." This attitudinal baggage mitigates against us when we reach points in our lives when we need to let go.

Fear of the unknown, fear of being depressed, and fear of pain are but a few of the many potential fears that prevent us from embracing "letting go" more completely. Letting go can bring at first the sting of loss, the pain of helplessness.   Yet what does Saint Paul say about his weakness?

LIVING CREATIVELY IN TIMES OF CHANGE

Moving from one stage of our life to the next can be seen as an art that invites creative transformation of our lives as we grow closer to God. The quality that goes into this art of personal transformation will determine, perhaps more than anything else, the eventual success of the next stage of living. We are called at every corner of our life span to live creatively. This takes on added dimensions of life and vigor in our senior years.

One of our most valuable skills of personal growth and change is our ability to listen, truly listen to all of life. This call to listen is not simply an act of the ears; it is more an act of the heart. Listening deeply can give us the valuable information that God is with us everywhere we go, by our side in everything that we do, whenever, and with whomever we may be. Listening lets us know that God speaks to us not only from the Bible, but from the beltway; not only in prayer, but also in people; not only in your community of faith, but also in our commitments and responsibilities. God speaks to us in every aspect of our lives.

Often, the shrill clangs of the world CAN drown out the steady pulsations from the Spirit that nudge us ever closer to God. Our lives are sometimes filled with so much busyness that listening is made difficult, and God's voice is crowded out. To listen well, we must calm ourselves and find the center of our stillness within. How wonderful the sounds of silence that can be heard from our central stillness. It takes courage to listen within, since we sometimes fear what we may hear. We fear that we may find only shadows and self-criticisms. Yet, we're called to go beyond this veneer of self-criticism and find that all-forgiven place that sings the song of peace.

The more we can listen, the closer we come to our true reality, the total Truth of who we are. We become totally present to God within, mindful that all is of God. We find that place of truth where we can see our beauty as God made us.

As we work our way through the transitions of our life, we find the gift of listening. Listening with our hearts to God's presence in the simplicity of life renders us open to creatively living our lives to the fullest. God speaks to us in places, and through people, and at times when we would least expect.

When we listen to our heart, we may eventually be able to hear the heartbeat of God, almost as through our own head was resting on God's chest. As we listen more and more deeply to this heartbeat, we may even come to realize that our heart and God's heart can beat together.

Here are some short stories that portray loss and change. As you read these stories, be thinking of how you might need change... how you might inadvertently block positive, life-giving change.

THE WOMAN IN THE WAITING ROOM

Janet stared at the ceiling of her hospital room. How could this be happening? It was only last week when she was in her doctor's office for a routine physical exam. It was when he returned to the exam room after her physical that he looked her in the eye with a look of gravity and said, *"Janet, I'm afraid I have bad news."* The breast biopsy the next day confirmed that the lump in her breast was indeed cancerous. Radical surgery was needed. Here she was one week later with her left breast removed and the surgeon's report that many nodes were involved; he thought he got them all, but he just wasn't sure, only time would tell. Right now she was looking at a complete regimen of chemotherapy followed by radiation treatments.

Tears rolled down her cheeks as she thought of the challenges ahead of her. She was filled with turmoil, fear, a disquieting sense of betrayal, and the hollow feeling that her life had just slipped away. And why now? Her husband Jim had retired only one year ago. Now that he was through the honeymoon stage of retirement, they were planning wonderful trips, new experiences, a bright future, and a renewed intimacy in their relationship. There was so much hope in her life just last week; now all was dismal... all was bleak and everything had become so somber. Her future had been snatched from her! She wrestled with so many thoughts and feelings. Most pronounced in her mind, however, was the overriding question, *"Why has God done this to me?"*

Days passed; she was now home again. Jim was attentive; her children gathered around her, all concerned and solicitous. She began to pray as she had never prayed in her life. *"Lord, take this burden from me"* was her only prayer for a whole week. Gradually her prayer changed to *"Lord, help me to cope; give me strength."* This prayer stayed with her for a long time. Janet wanted simply to get through the terrible travail of the chemo and radiation.

The prayer sustained her as she trudged through her therapies.

One morning as she arrived at the radiation treatment center at the hospital, she looked across the waiting room and felt the strange feeling that she was looking in a mirror. The woman across the room looked like her, she thought. Her head was wrapped in a scarf, as was Janet's. She appeared so much like Janet, yet something about this woman captured her.

Up to this point Janet was too angry to even talk with other patients she encountered in the waiting room, but today she felt a force compelling her to approach this woman. Janet found herself crossing the room and sitting next to her. Their eyes met, and with a smile the woman simply placed her hand over Janet's hand and said, "*I know where you are.*" These simple words seemed to open the gates to Janet's soul. Out poured a gush of tears so violent that Janet could not control herself. The other woman simply held her hand and continued to say, "*It will be all right. It will be all right.*" When Janet did compose herself, she felt better; some great emotional lump had dislodged from deep within her; she felt she could breathe deeply… a feeling she hadn't had since that fateful day when she was diagnosed.

Something shifted in Janet that very moment. It was like Jesus was talking to her, like she had encountered something divine in this simple, chance encounter with the woman in the waiting room. Yet what was it that changed? Later in the day Janet found herself in contemplative prayer. As she opened herself to God, she listened; she realized that she had been fighting the cancer, fighting the therapy, fighting the losses that had cascaded over her like an avalanche of despair. Somehow she believed that she had a right to be angry, she had a right to hate the cancer, hate the therapy, hate what had happened to her.

As time went on, however, something shifted at the very center of her core beliefs. Somehow the intensity of her anger and hate began to melt. Each day as she visited God in prayer, it seemed a bit more of her frozen attitudes about her sickness, her losses, her troubles melted into a puddle in her soul that seemed to cleanse her. Each day she felt better. Her anger seemed to be transforming into something beautiful, perhaps a sense of gratitude. Her hatred and fear likewise seemed to be converting from the stinging anxiety she formerly felt into a kernel of peace about to sprout in her very being. Janet was experiencing conversion. She had changed radically… she was no longer the same person. Just yesterday, as she sat in the waiting room, another woman walked over to her, weeping. Janet put her hand on hers and simply said, *"Everything will be all right."*

Kathy's Blindness

Kathy gritted her teeth in disgust as she swung around in her chair and stared out the window, reflecting on what had occurred last night. Her husband Frank had done it again; once again he refused to talk to her. All evening he simply stared at the TV, seemingly oblivious to her even being there: no words, no looks, just bald, sharp, and avoidant silence. This hurt Kathy more than anything else Frank could do.

Kathy was an exceptionally capable person. She had taught elementary school before she retired seven years ago, two years after Frank retired from his construction job. This cold-shoulder treatment from Frank was nothing new; it had been in the marriage for years. It's just that Kathy had so hoped that Frank would somehow "snap out of it" as he mellowed in retirement. Instead of mellowing, Frank seemed to intensify his behavior of withdrawal. Kathy was beside herself; she had tried everything she knew and couldn't see what to do next!

Kathy holds a master's degree, and throughout her teaching career she took graduate courses and in-service training. Frank was a journeyman carpenter whose formal education ended after his apprenticeship at the age of 21. Frank was embarrassed by his lack of formal education and was consequently very sensitive about it; he always thought that Kathy used her education as a weapon against him. From Frank's point of view, Kathy's ideas seem to carry more weight in the relationship than do his own. Her thinking on household management and purchasing decisions, as well as entertainment and travel, all seem to be very well thought out and actually pre-decided. Her stance on almost everything from politics to religion, from lawn care to child-care, from socialization to interpersonal communication, virtually everything as far as Frank is concerned, simply "counts" more than his own. To Frank there appears a clear imbalance, one that he seems either unwilling or incapable of handling. Frank sees Kathy as extremely competent, yet rather self-centered and even selfish; he feels she's the dominant one while he's the submissive one who always must defer to her. Her dominance is maintained by her efficient

Even Better After 50

management skills, by her persistence, and by her intense drive in wanting things done "right." Yet it's really Frank's under-active participation in family matters, together with his pervasive sense of self-doubt that pushes Kathy to take the "lead."

Frank feels that his wife sees him as a kindly slug, rather than as an equal partner; many times he feels like one of the kids rather than as her husband. It always seems to Frank that his wife really believes that *"Kathy knows best,"* that Kathy's way is the best way. Kathy seems genuinely puzzled when and if Frank comes up with even a modification to one of her plans. Her response is always the same to Frank; she's very polite but clearly patronizing, like a parent teaching one of her fifth-grade students the "right" way. Frank thinks he gets no genuine respect from Kathy. Over the years, Frank has become increasingly and rather silently resentful of how he sees himself treated. He feels he has very little if any power in his own house. He does love Kathy and even compliments her on her efficiency and effectiveness with almost everything she touches; underneath, however, Frank is angry to the point of being contemptuous of Kathy.

Because Frank is unable to address the issues of imbalance and disrespect that exist in his marriage, his "logical" defense is to emotionally avoid and psychologically withdraw from Kathy. These are the only "weapons" he has with which to "communicate" his displeasure and pain with the state of the relationship. Over the years, Frank became increasingly silent and intermittently irascible. All Kathy can see is Frank's behavior, and it simply seems that he is very angry and possibly even depressed. Kathy is so focused on Frank's behavior as initially contributing to the

128

breakdown of the quality of their relationship that it's hard for her to see her role in it. Her superior language abilities and innate intelligence is focused on relating Franks' faults to her own friends, rather than on her own actions and attitudes.

Kathy is unaware that she herself has become an almost constant critic of Frank. She's become resentful of her spouse, and blames him alone for the deplorable condition of the marriage. As far as she's concerned, Frank is the one who needs help, Frank is the one who has ruined the marriage, and he is the one who is wrong. Everything about her communicates these sentiments over and over. Kathy is blind to the real truth of the situation; Kathy lacks insight... she needs to change her perception of herself.

HARRY'S DEEP AND DESTRUCTIVE FEELINGS OF LOSS

It was 7:05 a.m. and Harry's alarm clock screeched to life, beginning its morning ritual. Harry peered through the slit of an eye opening to register that it indeed was time to start another day. For several minutes in the twilight of consciousness between sleep and waking, Harry felt very little if anything. As his awareness slowly emerged from its nightly hiding place, Harry's mind clicked to life once again; and as it did, that sinking feeling of emptiness once again filled the void as he "remembered" the emotions of his soul that he took to bed with himself last night, as he did every night for some time now.

For the last three years, ever since he lost his wife of 44 years, his beloved Anne, Harry couldn't seem to shake the loss of his life's companion and love. When the end came for Anne after a long battle with congestive heart failure, Harry was told that the mourning process would probably take a full year before he felt like himself again. Harry waited the year, expecting that the feelings of emptiness would be gradually subsiding as the months plodded on. Yet even after 12 full months, the gnawing feelings of pain and loss were as much with him as they had been a week after Anne's death. In that first year he had backed away from the friends that he and Anne enjoyed over the years. Several of Anne's female friends, who were now widows themselves, had called Harry asking him to accompany them to this or that social gathering. But Harry never would accept; he felt such a strong loyalty to Anne that any "dates" with another woman would somehow be a betrayal of the beautiful marriage they shared. He just couldn't do that.

Harry's life became smaller and smaller; it became more and more routine. Up at 7:05 every morning, get the paper, make coffee, read the paper over his oatmeal, feed the fish, and tune into the morning talk show. Soon it was time for lunch... make a turkey sandwich and clean up; head to the supermarket and find something for supper... followed by more TV, a nap, sometimes a short walk... make supper, have a Manhattan or two, eat supper, and fall asleep in front of the TV. His days could be measured like clockwork. Only on Sunday would he change his schedule when he went to church, always the early service, and scoot right on out again. When Anne was alive they would always stay and talk with friends after church; sometimes they would even go out for breakfast together with friends. Since Anne's death, Harry didn't have the "heat" for that kind of stuff. The couple of times he did go to breakfast, it wasn't the same as it had been when Anne was alive. He was uncomfortable; after the meal, he felt sadder than before missing Anne all the more.

He talked to his pastor once trying to explain the feeling he was having, but all the pastor could say was how wonderful Anne had been for the church, how beloved she was, and that Harry could find peace in knowing that she lived a good life. Harry's needs, his painful feelings, didn't seem to matter. Perhaps Harry didn't even know the words to describe what he was experiencing, and he really couldn't express himself accurately. Anyway, talking to the pastor like that it made him feel silly. Harry decided that he would just deal with all this on his own.

Round and round went Harry's feelings. He watched a TV talk show one day that focused on bereavement. He related to the program keenly because it explained how the bereft person needs to get back into the flow of living again; they need to re-learn how to start again. Harry heard the words, but didn't know which direction to go. How could he change his life? What could he do? He seemed so stuck, so unable to pull himself out and make any kind of real difference. The emptiness of his emotions, the pain of the nothingness and numbness ached every day. Harry found himself staring out the window more and more, and lately he noticed that his feelings were moving him to thinking that he too would like to leave this world.

INSIGHT QUESTIONS

1. What is your attitude toward change? Describe.

2. What do you see as the connections between change and wellness?

131

3. Why does any success involve loss?

4. What message of change did you see in the story about Janet?

5. What would you suggest to Harry?

Chapter Eight

Actualizing Wise and Positive Mental Attitudes

Actualizing Wise and Positive Mental Attitudes is the degree to which you develop new vision of the health tasks in maturing life, seeing them as opportunities for growth, achievement, and/or success, rather than as threats or irksome disturbances to your lifestyle.

Each of us is in charge of our own mood: we hold the defining power that determines whether today will be a good day or whether we will emotionally stumble and fumble. Living well, and being as healthy as we can be for as long as possible, rests to a large degree upon our ability to regularly affect our mood in a positive direction so that we can enjoy all our days, develop positive expectations, interact with others in ways that bring us a sense of connectedness, and create a mental atmosphere that powers us to make the necessary changes in our lives so that we can confidently continue our onward march toward growth and development.

At the center of a positive mental attitude is our ability to remain mentally fit: to be mentally tough when needed, to be alert to those attitudes that can drag us down, and to be vigilant to the quality and accuracy of the thoughts we put in our own mind. Developing a positive mental attitude also means that we use our emotions effectively. Too often we can let our feelings control our lives, especially when unwanted changes come our way. Keeping a positive mental attitude demands that we harness the power in our emotions by becoming an emotional dynamo converting the raw power of our emotions into constructive energy we can use in service of our physical, emotional, psychological, and spiritual development. This mega-ability of constructing and maintaining a positive mental attitude is *the* essential core of the eighth well, wise, and whole competency.

The Four Skills of Positive Mental Attitude (PMA)

The skills needed to possess a PMA include:

1. Confidence & Control

2. Positive Visualization & Imagery

3. Motivation & Concentration

4. Extending & Extinguishing Feelings

Possessing a positive mental attitude (PMA) is an acquired ability, or set of abilities, which give us a more or less continuous state of buoyancy in mind and spirit. PMA is the result of believing that we, and other people as well, are basically good. PMA gives us an optimistic point of view, accurate and appreciative thinking, and uplifting emotions. PMA is more volitional than you might think. Have you ever heard someone say, *"She's so happy all the time. The world isn't like that. Her attitude can't be real; she must be putting that on."* Such thinking comes from a person who has not developed a PMA, and perhaps cannot understand anyone who has.

PROFESSIONAL SPORTS AND **PMA**

One area where PMA is regularly studied and practiced is professional sports. Sports psychologists routinely seek ways they can help motivate athletes to perform at extraordinary levels, in extremely competitive situations. Sports psychologists believe that PMA, or what they prefer to call "mental toughness," is learnable. PMA is not genetic... we are not born with it; we acquire it. Since mental toughness, or PMA, is learnable, sports psychologists devise learning experiences where athletes can exercise and build up their mental toughness: positive thinking skills, mental endurance, and mental strength. This process is identical to what athletic coaches do; they devise learning experiences where athletes can exercise and build up their physical athletic skills, their physical endurance, and their physical strength.

Most coaches recognize that at least half of performance on the athletic playing field is "mental;" the other half is a combination of innate talent, genetic makeup, skills development, agility, physical stamina, and lots of hard work. Performance on the playing field of life, especially for persons in and beyond middle age, is likewise at least half "mental." Maturing adults need to learn the skills that give them the power to develop and use a PMA on their playing field of "total healthy" living. Our bodily functioning is clearly tied to our mental powers... to our minds. When our body is fed a steady diet of negative thinking, it will eventually react in kind by becoming sick. By the same token, when our body is regularly fed a nutritious diet of positive thinking, it likewise responds in kind by achieving high levels of wellness and well-being.

Building a PMA means that we must take up the challenge of self-control over the many connections of body, mind, and spirit. As we mature each day, our lifespan imperative of remaining as healthy as we can requires that we become ever more awake to our needs, strengths, weaknesses, and ourselves. Building ourselves and remaining as totally healthy as possible in our maturing years is very similar to what athletes must do, building themselves physically so they can excel and remain as competitive as possible. Here's how master sports psychologist Dr. James E. Loehr puts it in his book <u>The New Toughness Training for Sports</u>:

"The mastering of competitive sport then becomes a continuous process of self-transformation, change, and rebirth. Such mastery involves courage, commitment, and discipline. In short, it is a contest of each person against himself."

The parallel between the work necessary for serious competitive sports and the work necessary for living well in our maturing years is most clear. We are called by our faith to a process of self-transformation, change and rebirth; we call it conversion, redemption, and spiritual awakening. And yes, it certainly *does* require courage, commitment, and discipline. Possessing a PMA psychologically fortifies us so we can meet the ultimate challenge of living life to the fullest and maximizing our talents and potentials, as God wants us to do over our entire lifespan. We *are* engaged in a personal contest, an ongoing struggle between those forces within us that shadow our lives and make us weak, bitter, morose, irritable, and fun-avoiding, against those forces within us that illuminate our true life with God and make us strong, sweet, uplifted, cheerful, and fun-loving.

PLAYING A NEW "MENTAL GAME"

Sports psychologists study the mental attitude of athletes... called their "mental game." Too often, point out psychologists, the name of the mental game played by some mentally flabby athletes is the game of "avoid losing." The old mental game of "avoid losing" creates a mindset in the athletes where there is no joy, no delight, and no fun in the very process of the game. Athletes playing the mental game of "avoid losing" ultimately become mentally and physically tight, they stiffen up in body and mind, they become awkward and clumsy, they lose their grace and finesse on their feet; consequently the level of their performance suffers. In short, they lose their competitive edge.

Sports psychologists encourage athletes to adopt a new mental game of "playing for the joy of it." Peak performance comes from focusing on the moment, savoring the joy of the play; the best performance is not achieved by focusing on the outcome of the play, but rather on the process of playing. The new game means becoming 'play-conscious' rather than 'self-conscious.' This new mental game releases new and more powerful energies within the athletes, and it allows the best to flow out of them. Sports psychologists encourage athletes to find their inner calmness... the source of inner strength. Sometimes we can try too hard; we can demand too much and actually undermine our real strength and toughness from within. St. Paul summed up this concept well when he said, *"In my weakness is where I find my strength."*

> *As you play the game of life, is your strategy to "avoid losing," or is your mindset focused on living life to the fullest in this very moment, playing the game of life simply for the joy of it?*

All too often I see maturing adults mentally crawling into a defensive internal foxhole where they delude themselves into thinking they are protected from all the possible physical diminishments that could befall them. They are playing the protective life-game of "avoid losing." They become so mentally rutted in this reactive mental posture that it eventually consumes them. They become mentally and psychologically tight, awkward, clumsy; as a consequence their performance in life deteriorates. They find less and less joy in life, less and less satisfaction and meaning; their life revolves around their search for avoidance rather than a search for engagement, a search for living. Their PMA becomes deflated, and into the resultant vacuum rush the forces of shadow and/or compulsion.

Our thoughts flow, as it were, from our core beliefs. The maturing adult who believes that change is unnatural sees only threat. The current adversity represents a change and so it is immediately met by his mind with thoughts that say something like: *"This shouldn't be happening. This is unfair! This certainly shouldn't be happening to me after all the good I've done in my life."* Such statements seem silly when brought to the light of day because we can see how ridiculously false they are. To say that something shouldn't be happening when it is happening is only denying reality. Nonetheless it's precisely thoughts like these that can roam around our minds like mercenaries poised to strike us at times of adversity, causing so much emotional damage and discomfort, and destroying our mental toughness... our PMA.

STEP ONE OF A POSITIVE MENTAL ATTITUDE: CONFIDENCE
AND CONTROL
THE CONFIDENCE OF SENATOR AND ASTRONAUT JOHN GLENN

Your core beliefs form the bricks and mortar of the foundation of a PMA. Whether you are aware of it or not, you have beliefs about everything and everyone. Who is "in charge" of these beliefs? Your beliefs are not indelibly imprinted on your mind; they are not issued to you at birth to remain forever frozen. Certainly you've outgrown many of your childhood beliefs; you are called to change, and modifying your beliefs is a primary means for emotional, psychological, and spiritual growth.

The degree to which you take charge of your beliefs, the degree to which you can even control your beliefs, is the very first competency needed in our search for a PMA. Your beliefs about yourself determine your level of self-confidence or self-depletion. Your beliefs, or attitudes about everything outside yourself, determine what kind of a world you live in. When a person is said to have "an attitude problem," this means that they hold generally negative beliefs about themselves and/or their surroundings. When a person has "a good attitude," he or she possesses generally positive beliefs about himself or herself and about the world. When you can take control of your beliefs, when you determine what you wish to believe, you can actually influence your own attitudinal state at any given time. You have the potential for taking charge of your attitudes; you can generate a "good attitude" about yourself and about others. With such power would register high self-confidence as well as a solid self-esteem.

John Glenn was the first American in space. This feat of technical proficiency and courage was a triumphant success and earned Glenn a cherished spot in the annals of American history, and a warm place in the hearts of many. John Glenn went on to serve three times as a U.S. Senator in Ohio, where he distinguished himself further. At age 77, Glenn returned to space; he triumphed for nine days in orbit as a member of the seven-person crew of the space shuttle Discovery.

Glenn epitomizes this first competency of a PMA. Self-confidence is your positive belief in yourself. A solid PMA means that you consciously evaluate your beliefs, accent those that "speak" positively, while at the same time diminish those beliefs that tend to knock you down. In order to keep a PMA, you must believe in yourself by consistently accentuating the positive and diminishing the negative.

STEP TWO OF PMA: POSITIVE VISUALIZATION AND IMAGING THE VISION OF WINSTON CHURCHILL

Winston Churchill, former Prime Minister of Britain, gave a spellbinding speech at the onset of World War II when Nazis were bombing the heart of London almost at will. He said, *"When future historians look back on this time in British history, they will not call this Britain's darkest hour. No, they will instead call it Britain's finest hour."* If Churchill had gone on national radio and outlined just how grave the situation actually was for Britain, he would have caused widespread loss of morale and even panic among the people. Instead of outlining the threat, he rallied the people by reframing the situation as one of challenge. Churchill rallied them to meet the foe. History would eventually prove Churchill's words correct, and he would be hailed as one of Britain's finest leaders... the bulldog of Britain.

Here is a marvelous example of how visualization builds PMA. Churchill's words drew a picture for the people of Britain. His words removed the pall that had begun to descend upon the population. Enemy bombers and fighters were finding many targets right in the heart of England, in the center of London itself. Churchill sensed that fear was starting to infect the hearts of his countrymen. His well-crafted words gave his listeners the clear image that the people of England would not live in darkness, they would not live in fear; this was not a time to cower and moan. No indeed, this was a time to show the world just how stalwart the British people could be.

The picture included an image of the future: *"...in future times historians will call this Britain's finest hour."* There will be a future, we will get beyond this time. This is a time for rising to the cause. This is not a time for fear or complaint; this is a time for valor, for perseverance, for determination, for stamina.

Churchill's picture reframed the situation from one of desperation to one of potential mastery, from one of fear to one of gallantry, from one of separation to one of unity. All this in a few simple words! As Dr. James Loehr says, *"visualization is nothing more than the systematic practice of creating and strengthening strong, positive mental images."* Our brains interpret a sharply defined image in the same way that it interprets the actual event.

PMA comes from placing strong, positive, alert, and energetic images deeply in our minds; our minds latch onto the image and rally our mental capacities toward that image. Whether the image is positive or negative, our minds will respond by marshalling the full force of our energy reserves and focusing them onto the realization of that image.

STEP THREE OF PMA: MOTIVATION AND CONCENTRATION
THE MOTIVATION OF MARK MCGUIRE

What a baseball season! First Mark McGuire, of the St. Louis Cardinals, breaks the old home run record of 61 in one season, held for 37 years by Roger Maris. Next, Sammy Sosa of the Chicago Cubs duplicates the feat. Mark McGuire finishes the season setting a new record of an astonishing 70 home runs; Sosa finishes with a fantastic 66 home runs.

As McGuire was closing in on the record, the nation was captivated in rapt attention on this man who seemed to grow ever larger than life with each swift and mighty swing of his bat. Mark McGuire epitomized what a "real" baseball player should be; he embodied the soul of baseball. McGuire was the noble knight-confident, strong, sure, unflappable, and oh so dedicated. He played the game with chivalry; he carried himself and his lance to the plate with a grace and poise which held his spectators hostage, captured in a contest not simply between two major league teams, but between a man and a dream. The contest was so singular, so stupendous; the gods of baseball had chosen this figure from among the masses and raised him up to enter a challenge that seemed beyond the capacity of mere mortals. We were amazed by his strength, by his size, by his consistency, by his humility; but most of all we were dazzled by his motivation and concentration.

Motivation is the most critical factor in maintaining PMA. It provides the energy that drives us, it fortifies our efforts, and it powers us through frustrations, pressure, and fear. Most of all, motivation gives us a reason for continuing our journey, a reason for going the extra mile, and for reaching for new heights of life performance in the face of what others might call tragedy. Success fires motivation; yet what is success? When Mark McGuire was hitting his record home run in Busch Stadium in the heart of downtown St. Louis, there was a concession worker who was motivated to deal with his dying mother as triumphantly as McGuire was dealing with the home run record. Which of these feats was more successful? It's only in the eyes of the beholder that success is recognized, cherished, and defined.

When Mark McGuire walked to the plate his thoughts were not anywhere else but right where he was. His thoughts were not on the crowd, not on his batting average, not on the fit of his uniform, nor any other feature of his presence. His concentration was totally, completely, and unfalteringly upon the baseball as it left the hand of the pitcher. His concentration locked every muscle of his body onto only one thing... that ball. His entire being was cocked and absolutely ready to spring into life with a strength and swiftness never before seen in the pages of baseball history. The suddenness of the explosion of his swing, the fierce yet so natural uppercut swing, was heretofore unknown. His attention was riveted on only one thing, only one event, only one image; as his concentration pierced the din of the crowd, as it pushed aside all other thoughts from his mind, as it made its commanding presence known deep within McGuire's heart and soul, there arose in him a commensurate power equaling the penetrating power of his concentration, a power which uncoiled its ferocity when the sweet spot on his bat crushed the ball as it entered the killing field of home plate. Here was the magic, the spectacle, and the mystery of the man facing the potential of achievement made possible by a mental power of concentration unbounded.

Both motivation and concentration, the third competency set of our PMA, are mega-skills resident in our own thinking. It is our thoughts that determine what and how we motivate ourselves, and it is our thoughts that round up our focus and fling it at the object of our concentration.

Mark McGuire's thoughts created his immense motivation, and it is his thoughts, which generate the magnificent power of his concentration. How do you "think" your own motivation? How do you "think" your own concentration?

STEP FOUR OF POSITIVE MENTAL ATTITUDE: EXTENDING AND EXTINGUISHING FEELINGS
THE EMOTIONAL POWER OF CHRISTOPHER REEVES

They called him the "man of steel." His person is synonymous with Superman. His name was Christopher Reeves; as he rode his thoroughbred horse, so gallantly that sunny day through the steeplechase meadows of rural Maryland, he felt the breeze on his cheeks, the sun on his face, and the sweet smell of the newly mown lawn. What a great day to be alive! Reeves was well known and respected, wealthy, handsome, physically a Greek god, and with intelligence and personality to match. The scene was something out of a novel almost too good to be true. And yet this was the real life of Christopher Reeves.

As his horse rounded a turn and approached the next jump, the steed seemed to falter, he missed a step, and he lost his concentration momentarily. Just as the animal began his spring to vault the jump, it seemed to collapse into the barrier rather than clearing it with the ease it had displayed all afternoon. Christopher Reeves was catapulted over the shoulders of the beast, landing with a thudding crunch just beyond the barrier. As the crowd rushed to him, he lost consciousness, but quickly regained it to see anxious faces peering down on him, forming a canopy of concern. "Are you all right?" they asked. "I don't know...I don't know...I can't seem to move my legs," Christopher mumbled back.

The next day Christopher lay on his back in a hospital bed. He focused his eyes out the window, as his ears heard the incredible. *"I don't know if he'll regain movement. He's suffered several crushed back vertebrae. Right now he has absolutely no feeling from the neck down,"* one white-coated physician whispered to another who just walked in. And it was true: Christopher could confirm without question the last part about no feeling. Hard as he tried, he could not feel anything from his neck on down. It felt like he had no body - he was only a head.

The fourth competency for developing and maintaining PMA is having self-discipline over our feelings. We can do this in two ways: First, we extend our positive feelings for as long as we can and allow them to pervade our entire lives. Second, we extinguish our negative feelings after learning from them deeply and contain them in the one life area where they originated. Simply put, we extend the positive and extinguish the negative.

Our feelings can make or break our PMA. Our emotions can bolster our self-confidence and control, sharpen our visualization and imagery, and fortify our motivation and concentration. Or they can do the opposite – they can crush them all and obliterate our PMA in the process. We are in charge of our feelings, and it's this command over our emotions that spell the difference between having a PMA or having a NMA (negative mental attitude).

INSIGHT QUESTIONS

1. How successful are you at maintaining a PMA?

2. What is your mental game of life: a) avoid losing, or b) play for the fun of it?

3. Which of the four stories can you relate to the best?

4. Which of the four components of PMA is your 'strongest suit?"

5. What is the connection between PMA and overall wellness?

Part Three

Pathways to Wholeness

THE *SPIRIT* DIMENSION OF OPTIMAL HEALTH

Wholeness is the highest level of optimal health; it's the broadest vision of well being there is. Wholeness refers to a state of personal integration. When persons are whole they have personal integrity. Wholeness implies that the many parts of their lives are held together by unifying principles. This integration quality of wholeness allows them to live with an overriding sense of peace that this world cannot give. As we move toward wholeness we assume something of a transcendent quality where we live in this world, but invest our spiritual energy in the next.

BECOMING WHOLE

God wants us to live life to the fullest at every stage of life. When we *are* living life to the fullest, we are living in wholeness. Yet what does this mean? Does it mean having the most fun, the most money, the most friends, the most lavish vacations, the lowest golf scores, or winning the lottery?

Wholeness means becoming integrated. Wholeness is a condition of life where all our component parts are unified into one harmonious unit.

The opposite of wholeness is fragmentation, a condition where we feel like we're in pieces. Each of us has felt this way at some time or another – where life felt proverbially "on the floor." At such times we feel anything but whole, since we feel separated from others, from ourselves, and from God. We're like a bobbing cork on a stormy sea.

Part of wholeness in our maturing years is having a sense of control or influence over events, relationships, and circumstances of our lives.

We are not hapless victims of the forces that swirl around us. If nothing else, we have internal control on the impact of these forces upon us. The old adage, *"sticks and stones can break my bones, but words can never hurt me"* expresses how well we exercise internal influence. We can't control what anyone else says to us, but we do have control over the emotional impact these words have upon us. In psychology we call this "the elegant solution." Generally what *needs* change first is us.

Wholeness involves seeing all the events over the lifespan through the filter of our relationship with God.

This spiritual dimension of wholeness is the most central one for our purposes. This dimension carries a sense of being in unity with God. Our spiritual development never stops. As long as we live, the task of pursuing God, or pursuing wholeness, becomes our primary motivating force.

Wholeness emerges when our spirit, our connection with God, becomes the guiding principle in our lives.

We need to develop an unceasing commitment to become ourselves, which is the wonder and miracle that God intends for us. Life is, at its core, an ongoing process of developing ever-higher levels of challenge and more profound levels of satisfaction, whereby we increasingly discover a joy and peace that the world cannot give.

Perhaps the most rugged challenge in our present culture for mature adults is coming to solid conviction that there is more of "me" yet to become. Our culture seems to say that when we somehow become a mature adult, all meaningful growth is over. Instead of personal spiritual development and change, mature adults are supposed to simply "hold on," maintain, adjust, become content with resting, because our real life, our growth-filled, productive life, is over. From a wholeness point of view, this notion is absurd. It is only when we have the luxury of a personal history of successes and failures that we can embark on the spiritual work of growth into wholeness.

Wholeness is a perspective on life that allows us to learn the maximum from any situation.

Wholeness lets us see ourselves in this world in the broadest terms, where we are not caught in the minutiae of the moment.

Here we can take the global perspective and genuinely see the highest values and virtues that are there for us and in us.

Wholeness rests on wisdom, and wisdom is the spiritual product of living.

Perhaps paradoxically, and yet quite particularly, wisdom comes most empathically from the failures we have encountered in our lives. From success we can learn courage and confidence, but it's from failure that we can integrate the physical facts of our lives with the spiritual ideals that are of God.

Wholeness inspires us to harmonize both spiritual ideals and our physical reality.

If we focus only on the spiritual, we risk not being grounded in this current physical reality, we are somewhere in fantasy; we are not whole! On the other hand, when we focus only on physical facts, we become narrow in our outlook and very materialistic, inherently worldly; again, we are not whole. Wholeness is that elusive life condition that seamlessly binds together both the physical facts of our lives and the spiritual ideals that draw us to God's peace and harmony.

Even at those times when our earthly journey seems to be a relative failure on the material, earthly plane... in the light of wholeness it can be seen as a magnificent success. When we live in wholeness, each life experience and particularly our failures can produce a marvelous life understanding, a genuine message of unity in us, and a clearer recognition of the real priorities of our lives. Whole living is the condition of life balance.

The four characteristics of mature adults who practice wholeness are:

Chapter Nine: **Finding Natural Peace and Harmony.** Mature adults pursuing wholeness give their personal life energy to all the arenas of their life, not just to one or two. They see their "life job" as building the very best person they can from the raw materials they have been given by God and through genetic selection. They are well rounded, not personally lop-sided. They grow fully, like a tree that gets abundant amounts of water and light; it's not spindly or crooked, rather it's straight, strong, well structured, and verdantly balanced.

Chapter Ten: **Harnessing the Power of Purpose.** Whole maturing adults derive generous amounts of life meaning from their lives because they have a life purpose; they pursue a goal that is bigger than themselves. They live their lives "on purpose," recognizing that the meaning that flows from their life purpose can be the greatest generator of health, wellness, and happiness. They are people of faith, and recognize that their belief system is at the center of their purpose.

Chapter Eleven: **Living in the Whole "NOW."** Maturing adults who exhibit this quality have developed the means and skills necessary to realize that all they require for well being exists right now. They recognize that they themselves, and not anyone else or any outside forces, are responsible for their own happiness. They seem to keep themselves happy. They develop a certain detachment from the ills of their bodies and of the world. They don't focus exclusively on worldly matters, but raise their view to things beyond this world.

Chapter Twelve: **Honoring Your Real Self.** Maturing adults who can honor their True Self can view their past experiences as life advantages rather than as weights pulling them down. They know they have gifts and talents, and without being in the least bit boastful, they let their inner light shine. They generate a kind of spiritual luster by appreciating their internal attractiveness, and by making friends with their uniqueness.

Chapter Nine

Finding Natural Peace and Harmony

Finding Natural Peace and Harmony is the degree to which you give life energy to all six arenas of your life with some equality and thereby move toward building an integrated and stable lifestyle.

LIFE BALANCE

Balance is an attractive goal for us all; we all want to be balanced. For maturing adults, who are in or approaching their retirement years, balance has particular appeal since it offers a kind of internal retreat from the hectic pace of their former work lives. Balance speaks to us of harmony, peace, being settled... being in concert with others, ourselves, and with God. Balance offers the deep calmness that seems to be an innate and compelling drive of our spirit.

155

As desirable as balance is as a goal, it can be a most paradoxical and difficult concept for us in our mature years. For example, balance implies some level of contentment, yet when does contentment become complacency? Balance implies serenity, yet when does serenity cross the line into sloth? Balance implies integration, yet when does integration become self-absorption? What, then, is balance?

Balance can be defined in many ways, yet it's probably in our behaviors, and the behaviors of others, where we can get the most accurate picture of it.

- Balance invites a divine dignity into our lives, so we develop a long-distance view of our own destiny.

- Balance gives us self-control and invites us daily onto an eternal ascent to our inheritance from God.

- Balance gives us a contrite mind and a humble spirit, a tactfulness in human affairs, and a tolerance for the shortcomings and deviations of others.

- Balance motivates us to speak the truth, to seek well-earned recognition but not undeserved sympathy.

Jesus' own life was an example of balance. In the storm of controversy that swirled around him in the later phases of his public ministry, Jesus never wavered; he always remained aloof from entrapments. He answered his critics directly, clearly, and calmly, in understandable terms and free from the competitiveness of debate.

Our lives are a constant work of art, always in progress, always in process. We balance between-and in-body, mind, and spirit. One builds upon the other. In our early years we concentrated on our bodily development and agility. Soon our emotional, psychological, and intellectual development gradually required more of our energies. When we "hit" our middle years, our spiritual needs emerged as a new horizon of development. As we mature through middle age and beyond, our spiritual nature takes center stage as physical development abates and our intellectual development begins moving more clearly in service to our spirit.

Balance is achieved through a never-ending fine-tuning of our personalities, trying always to find a comfort level of harmony between and among body, mind, and spirit. Whatever comfort level we achieve, it can never be sustained very long before we feel a nudge of imbalance setting in, prompting us once again to find a more secure footing. Balance involves continuous attention to all three levels of human existence, moving toward ever-fuller integration of all three in peaceful and harmonious living.

Keeping balance requires that we continuously monitor the coordination between our internal selves and the external environment. We need insight into how we perceive ourselves, think about ourselves, feel about ourselves, and make choices for ourselves. Simultaneously, we continuously survey our surroundings, the events of our lives, our relationships, our behavior, etc. Balance is achieved as we regularly take in all these data from within and without and seek to adjust ourselves to find our center point. The degree to which we achieve these changes is the same degree to which we keep the flow of our health moving toward wholeness. Maintaining balance, then, becomes a fundamental factor in our overall health.

INTERNAL BALANCE

Internal balance is achieved best when we come to a full appreciation of our giftedness, our particular God-given uniqueness, and when we find suitable outlets for True Self expression. Our ability to express the unique personality that is ours, quite intentionally, from God is a primary dimension of optimal health.

God gives us gifts in the form of virtues (See www.healyourillness.com). Yet any virtue, any God-given gift, when carried to an extreme, becomes a vice: solid empathy can become drippy sentimentality; personal enthusiasm can become utter recklessness; and creative imagination can become impracticality. While too much emphasis distorts our gifts into something very different from what they were meant to be when bestowed upon us, so too we can neglect our gifts. Neglecting our gifts can also contort them into vices: hope with no energy becomes despair; wisdom with no attention becomes inadequacy; and steadfastness becomes unreliability. We need to balance our giftedness. Too much ego attention creates compulsions, and too little energy leaches the goodness out of the virtue and creates a spiritual vacuum in us – sometimes called a shadow (See Discover Your Spiritual Strengths).

As we mature and life transitions come at a more rapid pace, maintaining life balance requires that we become ever more nimble. Many mature adults mistakenly resist the changes they're called to make. Some mature adults achieve a life balance they're comfortable with, and consequently try to hold onto it beyond a time when it's useful and healthy. Consequently they find themselves stuck or fixated in a "false balance." Our attempts to keep this balance intact can lead us into behaviors and attitudes that are less than life-giving: irritability, isolation, frustration, denial, erosion of joy, self-absorption, diminished self-esteem, dependence upon others, overindulgence in food and/or drink, and an almost endless parade of quirks, tendencies, mannerisms, compulsions, and inconsistencies. Some of these coping strategies are simply bothersome, and others have catastrophic consequences. Depression is the number one emotional malady of mature adult living, and the suicide rate is highest in our culture among white males seventy-two years of age and older. Holding on to what "was," keeps us emotionally, psychologically, and spiritually off-balance. When we're off-balance, we become more vulnerable to insults to our total health. When we're off balance it's much easier for us to lose ourselves and topple over.

EXTERNAL BALANCE

Central to the concept of life balance is the fact that we function in different arenas of living. Each of these areas of living vies for our attention and competes for our energies. So, how do we best allocate our limited personal resources among the demands of each of our six life arenas?

1. **Our current "work."** The daily activities of our lives. Whatever "cause(s)" we have in life, that

which drives a person, the central life issue(s) that constitutes the "stuff" of a person's life.

2. **Family**. The sum total of all the relationships we have with family.   These include formal relationships with and as spouse, father, mother, sister, brother, aunt, uncle, etc.   However, they also include relationships with "special" people with whom you might live in close context and with whom we either give care or receive care.

3. **Relationships.**   Our relationships outside of the formal and informal family arena.   These include relationships with friends, acquaintances, service providers, neighbors, co-workers, church members, etc.

4. **Self.** What we think of ourselves, our self-esteem. What our image is of us, our self-image; our beliefs about ourselves, our self-concept; our thinking about ourselves, our self-understandings; our insights about ourselves, our self-revelations; our feelings about ourselves, our emotions.

5. **Spirit.** Our relationship with God.   Where do we see God in our daily life/lives? How do we talk with and listen to God?   How do we express our relationship with God?   What is our personal involvement with the things that transcend this material plane?

6. **Leisure**. That which we do when we don't have to do anything else, how we spend our energies when not engaged in the necessities of living (See chapter two).

External life balance is determined by the care we give to ourselves, how we fold each of the six life arenas into our overall life spectrum, and the ease with which we can shift from one life arena to another. Often we see mature adults overusing one arena, which has the effect of underutilizing the other five. This leads to anemic living and a condition of an external imbalance, something sure to take a toll on one's overall health. For example, it's easy for some retired individuals to load-up the leisure arena with little thought to the fact that they have needs in all five other arenas. On the surface, such a lifestyle seems free, exciting, fun, and well deserved. Over the long haul, however, living such a lopsided life eventually erodes the sense of meaning and purpose and renders us vulnerable to health compromise. We can become shallow in our interests, uninteresting to others, self-absorbed, prone to agitation or depression, and spiritually adrift.

Life balance takes on a heightened importance in one's mature years.

Balance comes from living a coordinated life on the outside <u>and</u> on the inside. On the inside we seek to become increasingly aware of our unique giftedness and seek ways we can express these gifts as God would have us do. As we find ways of expressing our gifts, we are at the same time opening ourselves to God's grace and becoming open to God's free-flowing channels of grace. When we ignore our gifts, we inhibit the flow of love and hamper our spiritual growth; we are not balanced, and we are not whole. The better we exercise our gifts, the more whole and balanced we become. As our wholeness increases, so does our holiness. God wants us balanced, whole, at peace, and in harmony. Reaching such harmony is the essence of Factor Nine in our journey toward optimal health.

BUILDING THE GREATEST PERSON POSSIBLE

The medieval story of a knight who loved justice provides a good lesson in internal life balance. He was known in his realm as a man of justice, fairness, honor, and deep faith. He was fair, just, honorable, and chivalrous beyond compare, and his attachment to his faith was likewise exemplary. He became so "on fire" pursuing justice that he set out in full armor one day in search of situations which required justice. He traveled from village to village, dispensing justice in its highest form.

One day he happened upon a village where a terrible crime had recently occurred. The mayor had killed a man in cold blood. It seemed without question that the mayor had indeed murdered the man; this apparently was common knowledge in the village. Yet no justice could be brought upon the mayor because he dominated the village as his own personal fiefdom.

The law of the land, well known to the knight and the mayor alike, was that all murder suspects were to be brought to trial for this capital offense. Yet the knight was unable to bring the mayor to justice because the mayor's henchmen prevented it. Finally in extreme frustration the knight cornered the mayor. An argument ensued; the knight became so enraged with the mayor's fraudulent denial and belligerent attitude of being somehow "above justice," that the knight drew his sword in anger and slew the mayor right there in the village square.

The knight, in his pursuit of justice, had become temporarily blinded to the very virtue that was his primary motivation in life.

This noble, God-fearing, and peace-loving man, who held justice above all else, had now become a murderer, one who denied and defied justice.

The Knight's pursuit of justice had become perverted; his desire for justice became so intense that in an over-zealous rage he temporarily lost self-control. In so doing, he had temporarily lost his grip on the real meaning of justice; he had passed the point of propriety. He surrendered not to the virtue of justice, but was captured by the vice of justice, mayhem. The knight had lost his balance and was, at that moment, not whole but fragmented.

Each of us can become out-of-balance, and we can temporarily forget our central giftedness. At times like these we become confused, befuddled, fragmented, and consequently act in ways that are not whole... but unholy. We can take our giftedness and push it so far that it becomes distorted the same way that the knight's gifts of justice became the vehicle for his separation from God and from man.

GROWING IN "NEW BALANCE" IN OUR MATURING YEARS

Our maturing years are blessed years because they offer abundant opportunity for injecting wholeness into our lives. Each of us has constructed our own personal balance in body, mind, and spirit as a consequence of our own personal history, as well as all our life lessons, insights, and revelations over the years. We are continuously called upon to realign our personal balance precisely because of the rapid changes that come our way throughout our maturing years.

Finding a balance in the ongoing work of personal change management becomes ever more important in our maturing years. Without balance we lose our way and never achieve the peace and harmony we so crave.

> *God is unchanging but not static; God invites us to constant growth.*

Peace and harmony only become our companions when we are nimble enough to adjust, develop, modify, and balance our personalities.

Change is one of the few things that doesn't change in our maturing years. In fact, change comes so fast and our desire to hang on to "what was" is sometimes so intense that we can easily fall into a defensive posture, where we try to push change away from our lives entirely. Such a posture places us at risk for emotional and physical symptoms, leading us into a condition of a personality imbalance. The changes that are necessary as we mature occur both on the body level and the mind level as well as the spirit level.

On the *body level*, we need to give more attention to our diet; develop a regular and appropriate exercise routine; and be more mindful of the ways that we use our bodies, approach sports, and rely upon sound medical advice.

On the *mind level*, change is also necessary. We approach our lives in more measured ways; we shift the perception of our own abilities. We may begin placing more emphasis on our relationships – becoming more patient, accepting, steadfast, compassionate, understanding, and kind. We may find ourselves feeling emotions deeper than before. We sometimes slip into reverie – remembering specific events, relationships, occurrences, etc. in our lives with new clarity.

On the *spirit level*, we feel the pulse of the spirit pulling us evermore toward God. We find ourselves in prayer more often, perhaps not formal prayer, more of a prayerful connection to God in gratitude, hope, faith, mercy, and charity. Healthy maturing people of faith become more contemplative; in the sense of focusing more on "things of the spirit" than on the material plane as they did in former years.

Our spiritual pace is quickening. We are accelerating the spiritual process of balancing ourselves on the path to wholeness.

As we do this, we move closer to our authentic selves, that which God intends for us. Here we begin to reap the fruits of personality integration, the ripening of wholeness in body, mind, and spirit, and the sweetness of true balance.

Since God wants us to live life in abundance, we are clearly charged with investing our God-given gifts in all six life arenas – and at every stage of our lives. The parable of the talents illustrates this so clearly. Talents are not merely skills but rather innate gifts, which lie so deep that it's easy for us to overlook them.

> *God wants us to be ever more aware of our giftedness and reflect our gifts with increasing accuracy.*

JUDY'S DILEMMA OF IMBALANCE

As Judy was at the sink cleaning up after the evening meal, her thoughts automatically pounced on the image of her eighty-six year-old mother sitting alone in her apartment. Once again, she felt that sickening feeling of guilt mixed with anger, sadness, and personal insufficiency. Judy knew that it was almost time for her to go see her mother for her nightly visit.

It had been six years since her mother sold her home and moved into an efficiency apartment in Garden Manor, an assisted care facility. She made two meals each day by herself and took her evening meal in the dining room. Garden Manor had everything that a well-appointed and magnificently managed facility could have. Judy was happy that her mother had found such a nice place with wonderful staff, well-manicured grounds, plenty of activities for her mother to do, even a full-time chaplain who visited her mom regularly. The problem was that her mother claimed to be utterly unhappy there. For almost six years Judy's mother never tired of reminding Judy that she'd been "put away." Judy had long ago ceased any outward reaction to her mother's criticism of Garden Manor, but internally she took each as direct "slams" on her competency, compassion, and caring.

Yet something was terribly wrong. Judy was known as the caring one among her three sisters; she was the one to take mom to the doctor, accompany her to the hospital, do her income taxes, see that her meals were there and her clothes were clean and neat, etc.; how could she be the one suffering from all these conflicting feelings? But she was, and she wondered aloud if she could go on.

Each morning Judy would visit her mother promptly at 7:30 a.m., just to greet her and make sure she was eating her breakfast. She would be back to share lunch with her mom and stay until about 3 p.m. After dinner Judy would return a third time for her final visit of the day, making sure her mother was calm and ready for bed. On Sunday, Judy would accompany her mother to church.

Even though Judy could agree with her adult children that her mother dominated her schedule, she just couldn't break away from any of the care she was rendering. Each time she would try to skip one of her visits, she would suffer acute pangs of guilt. She was absolutely conflicted in her emotions, stuck in her inability to claim even bits of her life as her own, and confined to a level of service that contorted her life and dominated her being. What was she to do?

INSIGHT QUESTIONS

1. How centered are you? How balanced do you feel?

2. How do you maintain your internal balance? External balance?

3. Have you ever had an experience like the medieval knight where you become so out-of-balance doing good that you actually did the opposite?

167

4. Are you currently building yourself into the "greatest person possible?"

5. How can Judy find more balance in her life?

Chapter Ten

Harnessing the Power of Purpose

Harnessing the Power of Purpose is the degree to which you can derive personal meaning from your life as a consequence of pursuing your own dreams, goals, quests, and/or life directions.

Becoming optimally healthy, in the fullest sense of the term, demands that we engage proactively in the great life adventure of expressing the monumental uniqueness that God has invested in each of us singularly. This lifelong adventure enlists every part of us. We need to focus energy onto our bodies to keep them in optimal running condition; we need to continuously feed our minds with stimulating thought, insight, reflection, and curiosity. Finally, we need to organize our lives in ways that place our minds in service to our spirit.

This life adventure requires power. One of the ways that we access this innate power is by identifying a goal, a dream, a life cause, or what we call "life purpose." Possessing a purpose means that we develop a desire and commit ourselves to pursuing some particular objective; we identify a singular point upon which we can focus the full measure of ourselves. This objective, or focal point, activates the vital energies within us. It moves us beyond ourselves and gives us a sense of mission, a reason for being, and a cause for living. This personal quest unleashes our power, synthesizes our energies, and gives rise to a renewed sense of well being in all arenas of our life.

Maturing adults have personal purpose in their lives to the degree that they derive personal meaning as a consequence of pursuing their own dreams, goals, quests, and/or directions. Maturing adults, no less than younger ones having personal purpose, know where they are going and can answer the big questions of their life, such as "What is life all about?" They have personally formulated life goals. They have dreams that provide "glue" for their lives. They invest in life change and spiritual growth as their lifestyle circumstances evolve over time. Persons with high "life purpose" generally have a creative streak that they focus in very particular ways. High personal purpose fires our imagination and leads us closer to taking on positive challenges in our life.

THE NEED FOR PERSONAL PURPOSE

Adults at any age want and need to feel a deepening sense of purpose as well as a sense that they are thriving and not merely surviving. Yet maturing adults of faith sometimes find it difficult to capture the full measure of meaning from their lifestyle; retirees sometimes have special difficulties. At every other stage of living, our culture provides us with rather clear expectations and responsibilities, both of which give us a sense of personal meaning. Such is not the case in the maturing years. There are few, if any, clear-cut directions that give focus to retirement living. True personal meaning is best derived from one's own personal decisions and actions rather than from one's environment. In our younger years we garnered personal meaning from pursuing more or less prescribed goals given from the outside. In later life, personal meaning comes more from within oneself than from the outside.

Our medical community has been very successful at not only extending life but also in making those extended years more physically healthy than was previously imagined. Mature adults are living longer and are enjoying immensely healthier lifestyles than ever before. But while we have been dramatically successful in increasing the quantity of life, we have not found ways to effectively fill this newfound life *quantity* with equal measures of life *quality.*

LIFE IS WORTH LIVING

Bishop Fulton J. Sheen hosted a television show during the 50s and early 60s called *Life is Worth Living*. He reached millions of people with a message of hope through his wonderful examinations of our faith and his encouragement for fully appreciating the marvelous gifts God has bestowed upon us. Today we may have lost some of this fervor that Bishop Sheen expressed so eloquently.

Even Better After 50

Albert Camus, the famous twentieth century French author and philosopher, wrote in his book The Myth of Sisyphus that, *"There is but only one truly serious problem, and that is… judging whether life is, or is not, worth living."* This question takes on special significance in our maturing years. What is the meaning of life when one is older? Life meaning is a universal need, no less so in our later years. But how can we find meaning, where are the means for achieving a meaningful life, a life that is full, rich, and satisfying in the later years?

THE MEANING OF MEANING

- Meaning is a felt sense; we *feel* meaning.

- Meaning provides us with a sense that our lives are "on target," that we are somehow living a life that is good, true, and even beautiful.

- Meaning gives us the emotional sensation that we are "in sync" with the truth within us, we are balanced and authentic, and that what we believe at the very core of ourselves is actually being lived out in our lives. In short, meaning allows us to feel real.

- Personal meaning gives us an expansive sense that we are part of a larger whole and that we are connected to a celestial order that gives us that wonderful security and stability of belonging. We feel that we are attached to something sure, something good.

The opposite of meaning is alienation.

- Personal meaning advances our spirituality in that we are able to connect with God's power and feel "in touch" with goodness at some level. We are inspired with God's power even in the way we look at God's earthly creation.

- Personal meaning allows us to feel part of an overall plan God has ordained. It deepens our faith, stimulates hope, and generates charity.

- Personal meaning gives us another gift, namely, to fix our vision on that which is pure and good, sure, stable, and changeless: the love in us and all around us. When we discover our personal purpose, we keep our eyes on the transcendent goal of life. We have faith in God and can therefore better shoulder the ambiguities of living life.

- Personal meaning offers us new levels of wellness. When we are focused, clear, and are living "on target" we are simply healthier.

LOSING MEANING

Many mature adults experience the opposite of meaning. They feel a gnawing sense of emptiness and meaninglessness. It feels to them like there is something missing, pieces of themselves that have been left behind, as if their "real" life is over, now existing only in memories. Such an emotional floundering represents a health risk of significant proportion. The sense of spirit and life that was formerly there seems to have evaporated or at least eroded. In such a state they can actually become ill, their vulnerability to sickness increases and their zest for life diminishes.

When we misplace our life meaning, we damage our health, diminish ourselves, devaluate our power, and dispirit our souls. Depression is the number one psycho-spiritual malady of the maturing years. In large measure this unfortunate situation is due to a lack of something worthwhile to live for.

> *The fact that mature adult males register the highest suicide rate in our society may be a direct result of a poverty of meaning.*

Yet it is neither in major depression nor even in suicide figures where we find the majority of the hurt that befalls us from the insidious poverty of meaning. Lack of life meaning is far more commonly expressed by mature adults in the loss of a sense of value, in a sense of frustration, existential confusion, unnamed internal turmoil, and angst. All this contributes to squeezing our lives and obfuscating our spirit.

SURVIVAL FOR WHAT?

Viktor Frankl perhaps expressed it best in his famous book, Man's Search for Meaning, when he stated, "The truth is that as the struggle for survival has subsided, the question has emerged: survival for what? It seems that ever more people today have the means to live but no meaning to live for." Jesus taught us, "One does not live by bread alone..." (Matthew 4:4). There is something much more to life than simply existing. At every stage of our lives, we need to be engaged in some challenging endeavor if we are to achieve "total health." Yet this endeavor is different for everyone and different at different stages of our lives. Theology professor Dr. Melvin Kimble contemporizes the words of Jesus when he asserts, "Man does not live by welfare services and Social Security checks alone."

Living Life "On Purpose"

So, where does this feeling-quality of existential well being come from? Meaning comes from the subjective appraisal that our unique giftedness, the personal talents we have been specially given by God, are in fact being expressed in our lives. These gifts or talents are not to be expressed haphazardly, sloppily, or randomly. On the contrary, they are to be focused onto a specific objective, some overarching goal of our life that is bigger than we are. Our gifts and talents are not to be scattered to the four winds in confusion. They are to be carefully aimed and executed like an arrow, deliberately drawn into the bowstring, delicately aimed, and precisely released to create the full impact when it finds its mark.

This bull's eye, this objective, this focused goal of our gifts and talents is called our life purpose. Our purpose, whatever it may be is *the* focus of life, the point onto which the full measure of our energy is directed. When we pursue a goal larger than ourselves, and when we express our giftedness to the full extent of our abilities, we are then "harnessing the power of purpose" and consequently experiencing the health-promoting quality of enhanced life meaning.

The fear of aging that seems so prevalent among us may be the fear that our later years are simply irrelevant, a fear that later life is a time when it is impossible to live a truly meaningful life. This fear seems to be identifiable at an ever-younger age. I once went to a party celebrating a man's thirty-fifth birthday. The "celebration" scene was festooned with black balloons, crepe paper, a black cake, and gifts such as Geritol, Ensure, Depends, and Fasteeth. If our image of aging is one of such decrepitude, is it any wonder that the later years have become so fearsome even for thirty-five year-olds? Where is there room for life meaning with such a dismal perception? Yet we know that such perceptions are inaccurate. The lives of mature adults are not destined to be years of collapse. Certainly physical diminishment of some kind is part of aging, yet discovering life meaning in one's mature years does not depend on our ability to perform competitive sports or possess robust physical strength.

We discover meaning by pursuing our purpose.

Measuring the ways we invest ourselves in the moments of our lives at any age is what makes life worth living.

Finding meaning seems to be a universal human need. A need is defined as something we must satisfy at some level or we get sick. This is a stark statement that points up the necessity for our search for meaning. Frankl believes that when we fail in our attempts to find meaning, we suffer a neurosis characterized by boredom, depression, hopelessness, and loss of the will to live.

Meaning does not magically materialize. Meaning already exists in our lives; we simply need to awaken to it. This awakening or discovery process is a central feature of life, a primal drive of finding expression for our own personality. Frankl further asserts that we cannot create meaning in our lives by thought alone; our thoughts need to be energized into some form of action. It seems paradoxical that on one hand we need energy to discover our purpose, and yet on the other hand, the discovery of purpose generates its own new energy.

WHERE WE FIND MEANING

Where and how can we discover our life-purpose and find our meaning therein? How do we approach finding life meaning? Dr. Kimble outlines three general areas where meaning can be garnered. These are:

1. Creative expression through achieving tasks.

2. Experiencing good, finding virtue.

3. A positive approach to suffering.

This categorization is immensely hopeful, so let's explore each of these.

We are most familiar with this first source of personal meaning – to pursue goals in the form of achievements and personal productivity. Here is where we seek opportunities for creatively exercising our talents and skills. We seek to find areas where we can express our unique personality traits and our developed competencies. Naturally this is a lifelong quest, a search for public and private stages where we can perform and show our genuine individuality. We commonly seek this expression in our occupational work, our profession, and our job. We select occupations where our uniqueness can be demonstrated and exercised. We also seek to inject our uniqueness into our work every chance we can. No two people do the same job in exactly the same way; they inject their particular style or personality into it.

> *We choose the kind of work that best "fits" us; we also shape our work to better "fit" us. In so doing we find meaning.*

The degree to which the genuine "you" is expressed in your work is the same degree to which you find meaning therein.

The second source of life meaning is the way we see goodness in our lives. Goodness can be found in almost everything. Even things that appear anything but "good" can eventually generate good. Very much good resulted from World War II being fought, even though the incredible tragedy of the war is overwhelmingly apparent. We can find goodness in a sunset, in a flower, in a sunny afternoon, and in a rainy day. Perhaps the most dramatic experience of goodness is in our relationships. When we can penetrate to the central core of a person and can experience there the light of God, we not only have seen the "good" that is there, but we have taken one step further: we have found love. Love is the highest form of goodness and the richest source of personal life meaning on this level.

The third source of life meaning is in our approach to loss and suffering. Here is the most hopeful source of meaning, for it is in the losses and suffering that many of us fall far from hope and goodness and even fall into despair. Dr. Kimble reminds us that,

"Life potentially holds meaning up until the last breath."

Just the other day a counselee of mine said to me, "I'm so glad I had brain cancer. If I hadn't, I would have never truly understood what life is all about." He experienced meaning because he was able to transcend the loss that was occurring in his life and focus instead upon the life transforming qualities that emerged in him as a consequence of his cancer. He claimed that he never loved his wife quite like he does now, and he described how his life was formerly a forum for competition, a place with only one goal... to win. Now he sees his life through quite different eyes as a place where he can exercise his gifts and bring happiness to others. He remains happy even though he clearly faces the real possibility that his brain cancer could reappear anytime. He reports a new richness in his life to which he was formerly blind.

THE TEN CHARACTERISTICS OF PERSONAL PURPOSE

How do we really know the degree to which we have discovered personal purpose in our lives? Average mature persons might not have clearly defined their own personal purpose in concrete terms; they simply live their life. Yet for most of us there does exist a singular focus that gives meaning to our life. We may not have clarified this central focus, yet it's generally there. Here are ten characteristics of persons who have high-level personal purpose.

1. **They feel they are living a meaningful life**. Personal meaning in life is an intangible quality that's very hard to measure; it must be experienced. Yet the subjective appraisal of the

amount of personal meaning in one's life is a good indicator of the presence of a personal purpose.

2. **They know where they are going.** Personal direction comes from feeling a personal mission, a cause, or a dream.

3. **They can answer the "big questions" in life** such as "What's the purpose of life?" "Where am I heading in life?" "What is my goal in life?"

4. **They have dreams.** These personal objectives are their dreams, the hopes for their life that provide the "glue" holding them together.

5. **They believe that change brings added meaning to life.** They are not afraid of change. They embrace change as the central wellspring of growth and personal development. They can "flow" and bend and be flexible in the face of change. They anticipate change and adjust their lives in preparation for these changes even before they come along.

6. **They have inner energy.** This energy may not be of a physical type – they may in fact be physically tired, yet they have an inner "life force" which ushers in a determination of mind and commitment of spirit which energizes them regardless of the physical condition of their body.

7. **They engage their imagination.** Imagination is not the sole province of children. Mature adults with life purpose engage in lively imagination, creative insight, and prayerful meditation.

8. **They feel a part of a larger whole.** Mature adults with strong personal purpose know that their presence here on this earth is intentional. They know they occupy a completely unique point on God's unbroken circle of faith.

9. **They experience an advancing spirituality.** Their lives become increasingly contemplative. Certainly, they interact in fellowship, yet they more often find themselves in quiet times where they simply focus on the awe and wonder of life itself.

10. **They maintain vision.** Mature adults with purpose can see beyond the material plane that is in front of them. No, they don't see "visions," but they can experience the presence of God in things that previously they may have only experienced as three-dimensional. At times, it is as though they experience a fourth dimension: the spiritual dimension.

FINDING PURPOSE IN ACHIEVEMENT: WAYNE'S STORY

Wayne turned off the light switch and closed the classroom door behind him, feeling a sense of warm wholeness come over him. At age sixty-nine Wayne could honestly say that he never felt better. Certainly, his minor arthritis was a nuisance to him, and of course, his doctor was always coaxing him to lose weight and get more exercise. Yet Wayne felt so good on the inside that his minor physical ailments really didn't seem to matter.

Driving home he reminisced about the personal confusion he felt a few years ago as he was readying himself for retirement. His entire career, Wayne had worked in the human resources department of a multinational corporation. He had climbed the proverbial corporate ladder from entry trainee, through local manager, to supervisor, to office manage, division chief, and finally VP for Human Resources. His success at his job was legend. Wayne had instituted many new systems and programs, always making their constructive mark on employee welfare. He was proud of his accomplishments and of the fact he was able to help people, and that his wife and family were proud of him.

The part he always liked the best involved hiring and employee development. He thrived on mentoring new people, supporting them, and seeing them succeed. This gave him a personal sense of satisfaction unlike any other. In the earlier and middle stages of his career, this developmental enrichment provided the dominant theme of his work. As he climbed the ladder, however, the dominant theme became downsizing, making the company more profitable by letting employees go. Oh, there were always nice, important sounding names given to this process, names like "right-sizing" and "corporate strengthening," yet the result was the same: people lost their jobs!

Wayne's sense of mission waned, his personal involvement in the lives of employees eroded, and his sense of himself as a builder, a decision-maker, and part of a larger whole dedicated to human development evaporated. Wayne became dispirited. His frustration with demands for higher and higher levels of profitability turned to anger, which erupted more than once into "scenes" at meetings. In time, it became apparent to Wayne that he himself had become a target. On several occasions, other VPs and even the CEO approached Wayne about his deteriorating attitude. Wayne didn't want to be asked to leave, so he quietly arranged for an "early retirement."

He'd never forget that first Monday morning of his retirement. What was supposed to be a time of rest and joy was anything but. For months he was all but unapproachable: Wayne had become depressed, his life no longer had any meaning for him. In time, a doctor's prescription for an antidepressant and a referral to a counselor began to turn things around for Wayne. He learned through the counselor that he was a person who needed to be involved in his church. First he attended several Bible study sessions, which catapulted him onto the mission services council of the church. There he discovered firsthand what he had only known from a distance: the suffering people endured even in his own city. Here was the spark that Wayne needed to take his own next developmental step. This step combined all the competencies Wayne had learned and polished for so many years, but now he added another factor heretofore quite underdeveloped in his life: his spiritual dimension. For the first time Wayne was blossoming spiritually.

As Wayne pulled his car door shut that evening after teaching a class on mission effectiveness, he was filled with that inspired knowledge that God's hand was on him, and indeed had been on him all along. Meaning had once again returned to Wayne's life, only this time it had arrived in a dramatically more robust form. Wayne knew whom he was working for and where he was going.

Even Better After 50

FINDING PURPOSE THROUGH GOODNESS: SHARON'S STORY

Sharon slowly bent down and caressed a rose growing in her garden. She closed her eyes to enjoy the fullness of the beauty that this rose offered in sight and aroma. Sharon had planted this bush some ten years earlier, at a time when her husband was still alive. She remembered how satisfied she felt that day. She had found the bush on sale in her supermarket's seasonal plant section. It actually didn't look very healthy, and Sharon bought it for half-price; it was all she could afford now that her husband was on disability. She brought it home, found the perfect spot for it, and prayerfully put the rose bush into the ground. The first few years the bush appeared meager indeed, but Sharon remained steadfast in support of it. In its fourth year, it seemed to draw strength from somewhere and exploded into verdant blossom. Each year thereafter the bush graced her garden and her home with blooms of beauty unparalleled in Sharon's memory.

Her husband had been an irascible fellow. Sharon married at eighteen, and became a mother at nineteen; she knew only hard work from the very beginning of her marriage. Her husband was a truck driver. His presence was punctuated by lengthy times away on the road. Phone calls kept them in touch, but Sharon's life became fuller as her family grew. As she looks back now it seems quite impossible that she had actually raised seven children pretty much by herself. When her husband was at home, his demands were relentless and his ire quick. At times he could become physical with her five sons, and a time or two even with her. She did leave him for a three-month stretch one time, but the needs of the five children she had in tow then pulled her back. After that, the children served as an anchor holding her fast to the home. Her marital relationship was incomplete, but she persevered, holding her husband up when he first went down with a nasty heart attack.

One heart attack led to several more. Still, she dutifully nursed him through them all and into his occupational disability that eventually placed him at home permanently. Each day she walked the gauntlet of his wrath of words. So many times her sisters encouraged her to leave and "get a life." The condition of her life, at least from the outside, seemed deplorable. So where did she get the strength to carry on? On a basic human level, where did she derive any meaning in her life? Where did she derive any purpose?

Sharon had asked herself the same questions, but the answer was always so clear. Early on, it was the children who kept her going, but once the last one was gone from the house the pull to stay was something quite different. Where or how she learned this had never been clear, but Sharon somehow was gifted with the ability to see the good in almost everything and everyone. It was not that she was a Pollyanna who was blind to the downside of life. No, she could quite accurately point out the insufficiencies in her marriage. Yet somehow, Sharon's vision always seemed to capture the good side of living and concentrated on the loving aspects of life. She reveled in her children, she marveled at the trees and the sky. The garden provided her with unending delight. Sharon seemed buoyed by life, not encumbered by it. She was able to see beyond the immediate uncertainty of her life and glimpse the changeless parts of who she was. All of this was much more real to her than were the more shadowy parts of her life.

Sharon's husband indeed had what we call in professional counseling a "chronic problem personality." But even with him, she was able to perceptually penetrate to his core, which she saw as good. Sharon seemed able to look right through his criticism, beyond his negative thinking and dismal appraisal of the world, to see something even he could not uncover under his self-absorbed demeanor. She could see a little boy pleading for recognition, screaming for love. In this picture Sharon found solace, she experienced a strange peace that was indescribable. Sharon's life was one of searching for good in God's greatness, discovering love in the strangest places, and finding faith in flowers.

FINDING PURPOSE THROUGH PAIN AND LOSS: MARIANNE'S STORY

Marianne inhales the marvelous view from the glassed-in-porch. The sky is what in the past Marianne would call foreboding. Today she sees the same sky quite differently. *"Soon it will snow,"* she thinks, *"and tomorrow the landscape will be all new."* She turns around her motorized wheelchair and heads toward her room. This has been her home for three years now, since she moved over from the assisted living facility on the same grounds.

It had been almost fifteen years since she was diagnosed with Parkinson's disease. She had mentioned it to her doctor when she first noticed that she was losing control of her limbs, but he simply encouraged her to "keep an eye on it." Actually she was relieved by his apparent casualness; she wanted it all to just go away.

When her neurologist came back into the exam room with a grim look, Marianne knew what he would say. It was then that she started on her treatment regimen for Parkinson's. In spite of tests, medication, exercise programs, and diet restrictions, the relentless erosion of body control progressed. Within a few years, Marianne was forced to retire from teaching. She took a job managing a small bookstore close to her home. Her knack for organization, books, and communication, together with her genuine love of people, made the first few years at the bookstore comfortable and successful. However, her disease was not abating.

In the fourth year at the store, she noticed very disturbing signs. It was hard for her to punch the right keys on the cash register, she had more and more trouble lifting even small parcels of books, but most of all she was always tired and in increasing pain. It now took her from thirty to forty-five minutes of mild stretching each morning to work out the stiffness enough to be able to get out of the house. Some days were better than others, but steadily she could feel her emotions sagging and anger raging inside. *"Why me?"* she would ask incessantly. Not only was she losing control over her body, she was also losing control of herself, and she knew it!

One Sunday at church, she noticed a small piece in the bulletin about spiritual direction. She called and found herself talking to a very compassionate voice. Mary Frances was the voice's name; Marianne was sure God had intentionally put Mary Frances into her life. Slowly, Marianne was able to bring some clarity to her predicament. Mary Frances encouraged Marianne to delve deeper into prayer. Her constant question to

Marianne was, *"What do you hear God saying to you now?"* This question reverberated through Marianne's head. It seemed to imply some order to all of this, some purpose that could be garnered from her sickness. Marianne could feel subtle changes in herself: the anger, the sense of loss, the confusion and aimlessness were all beginning to thaw a bit. Most significantly, however, Marianne was mysteriously beginning to sense a growing anticipation that something good was coming. *"Could this be hope?"* she thought. Certainly not hope for a cure of her Parkinson's; the hope had to be for something else.

She couldn't explain it, but one day she seemed to turn a page in her book of life: she felt better. She still had her Parkinson's, but somehow, somewhere, there seemed a sense of growth in the diminishments she was experiencing. She found a meager but definite sense of meaning in her physical diminishments. She was developing hope beyond them. Somehow her diminishments, pain, loss, and suffering were bringing some good... a strange good to humanity, to God's people in some unexplainable way. In this process there emerged some strength, some power that seemed to bolster her, even transform her into a new way of seeing and thinking and feeling. Marianne still had pain, she still suffered loss, yet now there seemed some purpose, and from this purpose Marianne felt the healing balm of personal meaning.

INSIGHT QUESTIONS

1. Do you have a life purpose? Can you put it into words?

2. When was your life most "worth living?"

3. How would you describe how you experience meaning?

4. In which one of the three areas covered do you most find meaning?

5. Which one characteristic of the 10 that describe persons with personal purpose most describes you? Least describes you?

Chapter Eleven

Living in the Whole "NOW"

*Living in the Whole NOW is the degree to
which you have developed the means
and skills necessary to keep your overall
morale high in all the arenas of your life,
by living in the whole NOW.*

The art of living well across the lifespan requires creativity.
It calls us to awaken to our dependence upon God for this
creative guidance. As we mature, we gradually learn that
it is not our own choice, agendas, or directions that lead us
down the most productive and growth-filled paths of our
lives and eventually to our true selves. Rather, it is when
we delve deeply into ourselves and there find God - and in
the silent, creative union thereof - that our true life
choices, agendas, and directions are most artfully realized.

IN THE SILENCE

We can hear God only in the silence. Listening in the silence of our souls leads us toward God. Listening to the silence affords us the privilege of walking on the outer edges of the lawns of God's mansion that already stands open and welcoming inside us. When busyness, urgency, and stimuli of all sorts assault us, in our hearts we can find the silence that gives us entry into God's dwelling place within us. We can always find peace even when the pressure of our lives brings us to the brink of becoming overwhelmed in confusion.

We can train our internal ear to hear the sounds of silence that harken God's presence in us. It is in this silence that the depths of our creative selves is stirred up and becomes most sensitized, receptive, and consequently most productive. We crave this shared creativity between God and ourselves; it lights the way to spiritual growth and development toward wholeness... toward the holiness of the NOW.

Listening at the deepest level of ourselves pays an uncommon dividend: happiness. Noted author and Trappist monk, Basil Pennington asserts, in the newly published revision of his now famous book <u>A Place Apart: Monastic Prayer and Practice for Everyone</u> that, *"...happiness consists in knowing what you want and then knowing you have it or are on the road to getting it. Most people are unhappy because they do not know what they want."*

How do we come to know what we want? Again, it is in listening in the silence of our souls that we come to understand our deepest desires. When we regularly listen within and enter into the silence, we come to know what we need. In the silence we can plan, in concert with God, how to move ahead in understanding and accurately respond in obedience to our deepest needs.

Retirement living, as it is most commonly practiced in our culture, can miss the mark of truly satisfying the deepest needs of maturing adults. Instead of supporting retirees in their quest for meaning and purpose, our culture seems content simply steering senior adults toward diversions of fun and play, which satisfy only our most superficial needs. Such a retirement lifestyle points to shallow living and leaves us wanting and uncomfortable, with a vague sense that something is missing.

Maturing people of faith, who wish to capture a more significant sense of living fully, learn to be somewhat counter-cultural in their approach to retirement... for them, prayer is essential. They regularly spend time within themselves, listening for God's direction. Their efforts are rewarded in the growing communion they experience with God. Where they find God, they also find their true selves, deepest desires, and most cherished needs. As a consequence, *"...the doorway to happiness opens"* (Pennington).

THE "NOW"

What is the "now"? Webster defines "now" as: "at the present time or moment." Yet, is there really any time other than "now?" Certainly we have a past, and we will have a future. Yet when can we experience the past other than in the "now," and when is the future considered but right "now?" The past lives in the present, which is where the future resides as well.

There is no other time but "now!"

If only the "now" exists, why is it that we must be reminded to live in the "now?" We have a penchant, indeed a compulsion, to compare. We seem fascinated by making comparisons, and perhaps the most common comparison that most of us make is comparing today with yesterday and today with tomorrow. *"What a beautiful day!"* one person will remark. The retort from another is, *"Yeah, but it's not as nice as yesterday."* Does the fact that yesterday was a beautiful day negate the balminess of today? Is today appreciated more or less by such a comparison? Such a remark discounts the "now," and squeezes out today by reinforcing the mindset of living in yesterday or living in tomorrow. There is no room for gratitude or appreciation when there is no "now."

The degree to which we "live" in yesterday or in tomorrow is the same degree to which we will be asleep to the beauty, richness, wonder, and holiness of the present. We can only love today; we can only truly live in the present. God intends that we experience life to the fullest and live it in abundance. It is in the abundant experiences of living and loving that we find reflections of God. God is present in everything and in everyone.

God is not past in everything, nor is God future in everything.

No, God is *present* in everything. Genuinely experiencing the truth, beauty, and goodness of the "present everything" necessitates that we ever more fully awaken to the God reality that is resident in the everyday present of our lives. We live in abundance when we live in the "now!"

Living in the "now" offers a successive awakening to God, of becoming ever more conscious of God. This can well be seen as the primary spiritual developmental task of our maturing years.

One of the most potent means for waking up to the "now" is through prayer. Pennington states, *"...the primary purpose of silence is communication, to truly hear God, to hear ourselves and others, and the whole of creation more deeply."* Prayer opens us up and clears away any worldliness that may be blinding our vision of seeing exactly who we are. Prayer helps us remember who we are; that we are first and foremost the daughters and sons of God. Prayer gives us a glimpse of our real spiritual nature, and in doing so jostles our memory back to our spiritual bedrock, our genuine reality in Jesus. Prayer is the vehicle that gradually moves us to a new high point where we can see the panorama of our lives in fuller grandeur and more detailed relief than ever before. From this vantage point we come to appreciate the primacy of our spiritual nature.

When we combine the power of prayer with an enhancement of wisdom that comes from patient striving for an integrated and balanced life, we can access the power of strength within us more cleanly and derive new direction, purpose, and "rightness" from it. As we grow in faith and more fully draw on the living water of strength within us, we quite naturally begin to savor the wonderful presence of God in everything and everyone. As we become more mindful of God's omnipresence, we develop

195

a new sensation of well being; we more easily suspend our criticisms and withhold our judgments.

> *As a sense of God's omnipotence dawns in our lives, we more clearly distinguish the colors of the beauty that surrounds us and honor the truth in all of creation.*

This marvelous mindfulness of God throughout our day sparks feelings of peace and brings us comfort and understanding even in the most tragic circumstances. Minute-by-minute mindfulness of God strengthens our tolerance for the ambiguity of life and gives rise to our creative acceptance of living in the mystery of God. Such is the mark of spiritual maturity.

AN ETERNAL ECHO OF THE DIVINE

Reverend Peter Verity states in his book <u>Out of the Ordinary: Awareness of God in the Everyday</u> that, "Deep within the heart of everyone there is an eternal echo of the Divine." It is here, he asserts, that we find our sense of awe and wonder, beauty and love. Yet, he claims, we can cover up this divine reality within us through fear. We build barriers designed to keep us safe from the barbs of living. These barriers are constructed to shield us from the emotional, psychological, and spiritual barbs that threaten our harmony, peace of mind, and psychological security. We erect these barriers unconsciously, yet solidly, not only to keep out the unwanted threats from outside but also to prevent us from penetrating into our own spiritual core. They block us from our true source of strength, the Divine echo within us.

When we prevent ourselves from experiencing the Divine within, we cut ourselves off from our true beauty, our wondrous and sacred self, the center of our being, the "real me" that resides within.

These are the precious yet vulnerable parts of ourselves that we seek to protect, because we are unsure that others will understand them. We are afraid that others may deride us and scoff at us for the very parts of us that are the most beautiful. Consequently, we hide them from view, and in so doing we also hide them from ourselves.

Verity calls this our "false outer shell." As we mature spiritually, we come to realize that this outer shell is both encumbering and distorting, and needs dismantling. How paradoxical it seems that we spend so much time building this outer shell, only to eventually realize that it is the very thing that blocks us from knowing our true self, because it prevents the light of Jesus from shining through.

Once that shell has been removed, we are free to show the radiance of God that resides in us. The radiance can shine through, as we gradually uncover our own vulnerabilities that we have so frantically protected over the years. Our maturing years provide us with a new freedom, new emotional independence, and renewed spiritual motivation to embrace our true selves more and more. We ultimately find freedom... we no longer have anything to hide.

Jesus does not call us to a place of danger. No, he calls us instead to peace and security. So how can we find peace and security by giving up the protection we have constructed for that very purpose? The answer, Verity points out, is that as we give up our psychological cover, we gradually adopt *"God's Word as our home."* Home is a place of safety and security, a place of warmth and understanding, and it is God's Word that can provide us this wonderful security. It is in prayer that we light the candle that burns bright and warm in our new home.

> *Some people never come to recognize that the barriers they have constructed for protection actually result in the opposite.*

The barriers hem them in, and they founder in darkness. Eventually, they develop even thicker walls for self-protection, walls like: bitterness, anger, irritability, shame, guilt, blame (both toward self and toward others), perfectionism, complexity, false righteousness, and passive aggression... the list goes on and on. For such individuals, the maturing years are not a time of shedding their protective outer shell; rather, they continue to build up layer upon layer like a candle being successively dipped into hot wax. They seem unable to light their candle so it brings light and warmth; instead, they seem only capable of making it thicker. Ultimately, they pay the highest price: they never get to know who they truly are, and they lose even themselves.

PRAYER

There are many kinds of prayer: praise and thanksgiving, petition and intercession, etc. One type of prayer designed to help make God's Word our home is *lectio divina*, which is Latin for "holy reading." The concept of *lectio divina* comes to us via Saint Benedict, founder of the monastic order that bears his name, the Benedictines. Michael Casey, in his book <u>Sacred Reading: The Ancient Art of Lectio Divina</u> describes the steps to this prayer process:

1. Reading: Taking the time to patiently and proactively read Sacred Scripture or other spiritual material.

2. Meditation: Letting the content of the reading find unique and personal meaning inside us.

3. Prayer: Relating better to God, the source and the goal of our meditation.

4. Contemplation: Listening to God's response to us as a result of steps 1, 2, and 3.

Casey outlines that Saint Benedict, *"...sees reading as one of the sources of spiritual energy, something that puts us into contact with grace and thus makes possible an enhanced level of fervor and unselfishness in daily living."* This type of praying comes from reading Scripture and other spiritual writings, not just any reading that randomly happens to cross our path.

Prayer keeps us centered. To be centered means that we are operating from the central core of our personhood. At this sacred center we find the wonderful giftedness that God has uniquely granted to us individually. No one else in the whole world is gifted in exactly the same ways as is each one of us individually. Each of us is called to let the light of these gifts shine. Indeed, the degree to which we recognize our gifts and work to exercise them in reality is the degree to which we will find happiness. Our gifts reside at our center, and prayer is the vehicle God has given us to penetrate into this gifted center. When we operate from this gifted center we are our most creative, productive, and fulfilled.

Each of our gifts is flanked by forces that tend to pull us from our center, and consequently, from our true happiness. On one side of our gifts, we find our shadows. Shadows are places where the light of our gift does not reach – places of darkness in our hearts. Shadows are areas of vulnerability for us in that they represent the opposite of our gifts. Casey quotes Aldous Huxley who coined the principle of "induction," meaning that for every positive force there exists a corresponding negative force. On the other side of our gifts from our shadows, we find our compulsions. A compulsion is the perversion of a gift, when we bring our gift to a distorted and contorted condition, and we then use this contorted "gift" to bring glory to ourselves rather than to God.

An example might be illuminating. People who have been gifted with <u>wisdom</u> become vulnerable to the shadow of <u>inadequacy</u> and the compulsion of <u>perfectionism</u>. The continuum is shown in the following diagram:

Perfectionism	**WISDOM**	Inadequacy

Their personality is vulnerable to inadequacy and perfectionism at either extreme of the center position of wisdom. When they move either toward inadequacy or toward perfectionism, they move away from their gifted center of wisdom and hence become un-centered, or unbalanced. In such a condition, they become figuratively separated from God and function in an insufficient manner; they become spiritually unstable and feel personally fragmented and spiritually distant from God.

Prayer reminds us of whom we are at our center. Prayer energizes our true selves and allows us to be who we really are, not some facsimile of ourselves, but the original creation that God made uniquely and intentionally as such. Prayer, then, brings us to ourselves in this moment, not yesterday or tomorrow, but right now. Prayer integrates us and provides us with the living water of God, the water that refreshes us like nothing else. Here is where we find ourselves living in the whole "NOW!"

THE THREATS TO PRAYER: EMILY'S BUSY LIFE

Emily is a good person. The mother of three children, she is intensely interested in their welfare. Her youngest is Bret, now seventeen and a junior in high school. Bret is a great kid. He is a class officer, on several sports teams, socially active, and a musician to boot. Emily was always wholeheartedly involved in all her children's lives, but because Bret is her last, and the only one still at home, she is particularly involved in his life. Emily serves as a class advisor, she is active in several volunteer activities at Bret's school, and also occupies the fund-raising chairperson position for the junior/senior prom. On top of this, Emily holds down a full time job at which she excels.

Having started her family somewhat late, Emily is now sixty years old. She is as healthy, active, vital in every way, participatory, and extroverted. Bret is a chip off his mother's shoulder in the socialization department. Emily has many, many friends; she and her husband Hank maintain a full social schedule. Emily is so involved that it is a rarity to find her at home on almost any night. She rushes home from work, throws dinner together, interacts with Bret and Hank, and off she goes to a meeting or whatever. Busyness seems to be in the very fabric of her personality.

Emily knows that she should pray, she even wants to pray, yet she never seems to find the time to quiet her mind and sooth her soul by praying. One time several years ago, Emily resolved to pray more. She thought the morning would be the best time... greet the day by remembering God. What she did was to set the alarm fifteen minutes earlier in the morning for this purpose. After only two days her staunch resolution dissolved when Bret needed a ride to the airport. After she missed only one day, she couldn't summon-up the necessary stamina to keep her prayer life alive. Later she tried to extend her day by fifteen minutes to spend in prayer just before she went to bed. Unfortunately she tried praying while in her nightclothes and in bed. As you might have guessed, that didn't last for even the first fifteen-minute session.

Emily is a practical person; she likes to be efficient and effective in all that she does. Unfortunately, her practicality seems to favor things of this world, things that she can see. Such things mean more to her than do issues of the soul, which cannot be seen through human eyes. Consequently, Emily's values system holds worldly, physical things dearer than anything else. These are the things, the people, the activities, the competition, the social events, and all the rest, that occupy Emily all but exclusively.

Gradually, Emily has unconsciously downgraded matters of the soul to the point where they hardly seem relevant to her at all. Oh, she still goes to church on Sunday, more or less regularly, yet her mind is only rarely focused on the service. More often than not, her mind is racing with what she wants, or needs, or would like to get done in various arenas outside of her spiritual life. God seems to have been edged out of her life, even though she doesn't want this at all.

Emily has fallen into a trap that is all too common in our harried days. There are so many distractions that distort our lives and cause us to lose the very core of who we are. Emily's condition very much reflects that of many of us. We want to pray, we want to be close to the Lord, yet we seem swept into the busyness of the times to the degree that we forfeit our true selves to the illusionary push of getting things done, trying to experience all there is to experience. We seem a culture full of Marthas rather than one that values Mary.

Finding time for prayer is the wrong approach. Finding time indicates that all else is more important, and if we can squeeze prayer into our otherwise busy schedule then we have succeeded. Rather than finding time for prayer, try to *make* time for prayer. Making the time for prayer infers that we start out with prayer first; after prayer we fill in our schedule with all the other issues, tasks, responsibilities, and desires that take the rest of our day. Living in the NOW demands that we seek the kingdom of God first.

Even Better After 50

DISCOVERY OF SILENCE

Phil retired five years ago. Since then, he has undergone a significant change in his life; one could even call it a conversion. During his working years, Phil was always the busiest of the busy. There was no end to the projects he could create. His penchant for project creation was not confined to work. He was equally, if not more, inclined to manufacture projects around the house as well. *"Idle hands are the devil's workshop,"* was an adage that applied keenly to Phil; his hands were never idle. Like Tarzan swinging through the jungle from vine to vine, Phil swung through his life from project to project... never missing a beat in the exaggerated tempo of his life.

Shortly after his retirement, Phil extended his workaholic ways to his new lifestyle. He never seemed particularly unhappy, but he lived in an intensity of productivity that appeared to block out any potential for real personal interaction with others or with God. Then, one day when Phil was walking down the steps to his workshop, a sharp pain startled him in his chest. Two hours later, he found himself in the emergency room. The doctor at his bedside explained that he had experienced a heart attack. Phil was lucky in that there wasn't much permanent damage. He would survive, but his lifestyle had to change.

In eight weeks of cardiac-rehabilitation, Phil gradually was able to take some big steps away from his hyper-paced life. He came to realize that his frenetic lifestyle had not only pushed him to the brink of his physical and emotional tolerance, but it was probably a big causative factor of his heart attack as well.

Even more startling, his heart attack jolted Phil from the deep psychological sleep in which he had slumbered for so long. This sleep was not an actual physical sleep; rather, it was a sleep caused by such intense interest in his projects that he was unaware of the wonder and the delight that existed right in front of him. His wife, Mary, had tried to get Phil's emotional attention, only to be disappointed time and time again by Phil's personal entrapment in "doing."

Phil now clearly understood that he needed to dramatically modify his lifestyle. The heart attack had gotten his attention, and it had wrenched him away from his previous beliefs about life and living. He wasn't quite clear about how he could change his life, nor was he clear about what he was to become. Phil did know, however, that he needed to switch the major focus of his life away from the busyness of his projects and onto a more enlivened awareness of his own needs, emotionally, psychologically, and spiritually, as well as Mary's needs. He needed to refocus his actions; he had been stuck in a tunnel-vision way of living, which blocked him from fully experiencing the joy, delight, and wonder of today.

Phil decided to talk to his pastor, who in turn referred Phil to a spiritual director. There he learned the value of silence. The spiritual director "prescribed" a daily regimen of prayer, meditation, and most of all, time for silence... time for listening. At first, this was more than anxiety provoking for Phil. Gradually, however, he learned to discipline his nature into the silence and away from all his worldly projects. In time, Phil found himself actually looking forward to his daily "walk" with God.

Phil would meet God in the silence deep within himself.

Usually, he would silently read Scripture, then he would think about its meaning for his life. Next, he would talk to God in his heart, and finally grant himself ten minutes of silence, in which he would simply listen for God in his own depths.

Gradually, Phil learned the value and the benefits of silence and, strangely, as he progressed in his listening to God regimen, he noticed that he had come to enjoy his much more balanced projects all the more.

FINDING THE WHOLE "NOW"

One of the rich lessons of a maturing life is the developing wisdom that life can only be lived in the "now." In the wonderful poem by Ana Jaramello entitled *I Am,* God is called the great "I Am." This means that God dwells in the eternal present. God is not "I was." God is not in yesterday. God is not "I will be." Again, God is not to be found tomorrow. It is only in today, in the current moment, where we find God. It is only today when we receive grace, and only today when we can express love. Today, right now, is the most important time there could possibly be; now is the only time you can live.

TED

Ted is a retired engineer; indeed, he was a most successful engineer, having worked for the U.S. Army Corps of Engineers for almost his entire career. His specialty was building dams and locks for river projects in the upper Midwest states. He rose to become chief of the

Midwestern area office. When he retired, he had accumulated many accolades for his leadership and multiple commendations for his fine engineering accomplishments. There was no question that Ted was an "engineer's engineer." He was a proficient professional, if not a somewhat perfectionistic, civil engineer.

Now that Ted is retired, his activities are sparse indeed. During his extensive working years, it seems that he gave himself very little time for developing outside interests: no hobbies, no sports interests, no civic, social, or fraternal organization memberships, and actually very little at church, except his perfunctory attendance on Sunday mornings. The only organizations he actively participated in were professional civil engineer associations. Yet, even with these, he has now let his memberships lapse.

The one pleasure Ted does enjoy is that every morning he appears sharply at 7:15 at a local restaurant for breakfast. There he meets two other retired men with whom he "chews the fat." All of these men seem cut from the same cloth: they were extremely consumed by their careers during their working years and have found little else to give them any sense of self, recognition, acceptance, or commendation in their retirement. Consequently, the conversation at breakfast each morning consists of stories from their working years. They seem to never tire of hashing and rehashing stories from the past. Each of the men seems to have his favorite years, where he felt himself "on top of his game."

Ted is living in the past. His conversation proves over and over again that his mind is stuck somewhere in the past. It seems as though he refuses to live in the "now." Ted's view of his present life is one of resignation. He sees no challenge in today; he sees no opportunity for accomplishment, no chance for confirmation or reward. He believes all of this is behind him, lost in the past. Consequently, he tries to relive the past every chance he can. His sense of self is marooned at some former place in time, when he saw himself as vital, productive, and generative... the very things he can't see in himself today. Ted's attitude toward aging, and hence toward his retirement, has pushed him "over the hill."

Ted's attitude gives him the excuse to believe that today is not worth as much as yesterday; for Ted, it was yesterday when he was at his best. He believes at his core that no longer does he have to "put his best foot forward," exert himself, try anything new, think new thoughts, or challenge himself – all because his best times were long ago. Ted will undoubtedly continue to meet with his two friends for breakfast each morning, trying desperately to gain some level of self-esteem by selectively remembering his yesterdays, and all the while discounting his life and his capacity for loving today.

GIFTS OF THE WHOLE "NOW"

What actually happens to us as we grow ever closer to truly living in the "now?" What gifts or signs can we recognize which might give us an indication that we are indeed finding our true selves in the "now," in silence, in mindfulness, in prayer? Certainly, everyone experiences a spiritual life in different ways, yet there are commonalities that serve as evidence that we are on the right path. The following markers of "now living" manifest themselves in many ways. These are more common among persons who can find beauty and strength in their relationship with God in the "now."

1. **Overall Good Mood.** When we see the beauty of what is right in front of us, when we recognize God in everyone and everything, there emerges in us that wonderful "good cheer" that Jesus referred to so many times in Scripture. It is we, ourselves, who are in charge of our own overall morale. Prayer, listening to God, and spiritual meditation all serve to bolster our mood and deepen our sense of well being. Prayer helps us rid ourselves of any grudges that may have blocked our spiritual growth and our emotional balance.

2. **Personal Control.** Developing mindfulness of the presence of God, and delving deeply into ourselves in prayer, gives rise to a sense of mastery over life. It is not that we compulsively exercise control over persons and things around us; it is rather that there rises in us a sense of balance and "rightness." Regularly retreating from the world and finding the silence that is God within raises our sense of self-mastery, our sense of self-agency; we become more forthright and more confident.

3. **Humility.** Persons who make the time for prayer, for reading Scripture (and other spiritual reading material), and for listening to God's Word in the silence of their world, are also the ones who can recognize and act upon their physical, psychological, and spiritual needs. They are persons who come to know themselves well and can care for themselves with great kindness.

Consequently, they more fully meet their health needs; their ego needs of acceptance, recognition, and achievement; and their spiritual needs of finding meaning and sacred fulfillment in their daily lives.

4. **Live a "Richer" Life.** Living richly does not depend upon our material lifestyle. Living richly refers to the sense of personal satisfaction that we derive from living. Living richly means that we find deep meaning in our lives, that we have direction, purpose, and life cause. We know where we are and who we are, we know we are "on track" with our lives, and have a sense that this very moment is a link in a spiritual chain that we are constructing that eventually leads to Jesus.

Living in the "now" gives us a home in God's Word... in God's promise.

INSIGHT QUESTIONS

1. How often do you "go" to prayer? How much time do you devote to silent prayer?

2. How do you experience the "now?"

3. How much of your thinking is in the past? The future?

4. What barriers prevent you from experiencing the "now" more often?

5. How much are you like Emily? Phil? Ted?

Chapter Twelve

Honoring Your Real Self

*Honoring Your Real Self is the degree to
which you view your life experience as a
life advantage, and enjoy successively
discovering your authentic self, owning
your spiritual luster, and progressively
journeying toward wholeness.*

WHAT IS THE "WHOLE" SELF?

What is our *Whole Self*? Standing erect and balanced at
the center of each of us lives our most real self, our most
authentic self, and our most genuine self. This self has
been called the "Self with a capital S," to distinguish it
from our ego self that merely masquerades as our genuine
self, but is actually only a concocted shadow of the self,
designed to serve the illusionary forces that inhabit us.

As the *whole self* is firm and steady, our ego self is quite
fluid and changeable. We may even develop several

fabricated selves that we extrude from our imagination and project upon the screen of our lives. If we are endowed with a real or *Whole Self*, then there must be fragments of it, echoes of it, distorted reflections of it, which we somehow assemble in order to create an image of self that we would like to portray in particular circumstances.

> *Yet, life is not a masquerade. It is a journey of discovery of who we really are, a journey in search of our Whole Self.*

Healthy maturation offers us a wonderful gift. With advancing maturity, we progressively come to understand and deal with the defenses we constructed over the years and relied upon for self-definition. We begin to let go of the illusions that our ego formerly erected as self-protective devices.

In youth we strove for such things as physical prowess, power, status, wealth, idealized love, and ultimate personal fulfillment as a means to fortify and strengthen us... to make us worthy in the eyes of others and ourselves. In our youthful thinking, we saw these things as "us." It is not until we advance beyond such thinking that we come to recognize these things for what they are: not personal saviors, but simply hollow facades, diversionary, "plastic gods" we worshiped in vain. Thus, we can disassemble them, brick-by-brick, and let the true light of our Whole Self come shining through.

A TREK TOWARD AUTHENTICITY

Thomas Merton says that life is a personal trek toward greater levels of personal authenticity. This trek is sometimes straight and intentional, but more often it meanders to and fro with little direction at all. The markers along the way are often unidentifiable, and we can feel lost and confused, depressed, and even despairful.

> *Our Whole Self, or Holy Self, speaks to us always, yet in ways that might seem cryptic at first.*

Along the trek we encounter, at random times and in ordinary places, surprising events which capture our attention momentarily and excite something deep inside us. Such events are fleeting, and we can often lose them among the pressures of life. Yet they linger in our mind subconsciously – only to reemerge in our prayer as "holy instants"... that is, times when we actually realize that the hand of God touches us in a most direct way.

In the quiet of our soul, we recognize that we were, at such times, treading on holy ground; something sacred inside of us is speaking, nudging, pointing out a direction into more noble territory, more abundant living, and giving us in the process a clearer picture of who we really are. These are the marvelous times when we catch glimpses of our *Whole Self*. Such glimpses become memories of hope and trust in the world, they further align us with the values that our *Whole Self* uses to beckon us closer to God.

In her book, <u>When the Heart Waits</u>, Sue Monk Kidd speaks eloquently of the *Whole Self* when she says: *"I realized that the heart of religion was setting up an honest dialogue with the uniqueness of one's soul and finding a deeply personal relationship with God, the inner Voice, the inner Music that plays in you as it does in no one else."* Her description of "...the uniqueness of one's soul" is a reference to the *Whole Self*. It plays music to us, and this music is from God. The degree to which we can dance to this music is determined by how well we are willing to let the maturation process be our friend, to whisk us off the dance floor of our false self and onto God's dance floor.

If we could only do this or achieve that... if only we could be more energetic, smarter, cleverer, richer, better looking, etc. Our ego self spins erroneous mental and emotional webs that only serve to confuse us and pull us away from our *Whole Self*. The logic of our ego self tries to convince us that if we could only get rid of the "bad" stuff in our lives (this includes people who we don't agree with us, circumstances we don't like but can't change, parts of our bodies that likewise we can't change, failures, losses, and all other manner of issues that are simply part of living) we would be left with only the "good" parts of ourselves, and go on to live a worry-free life that would be more pleasing to God. Ah, the perfectionist's delight! But such logic is fallacious; it sets us apart from others, rather than bringing us into loving connection with them. It sets up a legalistic standard of "shoulds" and "should-nots," fundamentally separated from the Gospel of Jesus Christ.

THE PARADOX OF WHOLE SELF

The awesome paradox of the *Whole Self* is that is does not discard any part of us; rather, it integrates all parts of our being and uses each to bring greater glory to God and happiness to ourselves.

We live in a tension between the power of God and the enticement to live without God.

At first, it seems prudent to remove those parts of us that incline us to forget God. However, this is impossible. We are supposed to live in tension, because we can only grow toward God when we are in tension. Remove the tension, and we stop growing; we quit the journey toward God and the possibility of finding our *Whole Self*.

How strange to admit that we need our false selves, those parts of us that we would rather not have, in order to find the *Whole Self*. Discovering this self is a lifelong journey of integrating the truth, beauty, and goodness with which God made us. We are called to embrace all parts of ourselves, both the noble and ignoble. By following such a path, our meandering is straightened, and our journey finds direction. We may still feel inclined toward transgression, yet gradually the intensity of the transgression and/or the duration we spend in it lessens. With spiritual discipline we can eventually reach an awareness that our vulnerability to the transgression's potential can actually become a valuable part of us. As we mature, our vulnerability lessens and we seldom, if ever, find ourselves acting out our potentials for transgression. We learn to integrate impulses of ego transgression into our being and redirect the energy toward our ultimate well being.

When we do manage to rise above one tension, another is sure to fall into its vacant slot; should we surmount one compulsion, another is ready to replace it. This is not because God is a vengeful, sinister, or torturing God – quite the contrary. In our present state of existence, it is through tension that we grow in the wisdom that moves us closer to God and closer to our *Whole Self*.

> *The paradox is that, in order to find our*
> *Whole Self, we must live in tension.*

The life of Jesus was not a model of stress-free existence; wherever he went, he brought both peace and tension. Jesus brought peace through healing, but he also brought contention through rebuking. He set up dramatic choices for people: *"If you love me, keep my commandments."* To the rich man he said, *"Sell all that you own, give it to the poor, and follow me."* Do you think that either of these two statements created peace? Certainly not at the moment, the peace they would bring was far off. We must first slog through the tension of the moment. Life starts with the tension of birth and will end with the tension of death. In between, we find innumerable events and experiences replete with tension. All of these, when recognized as the growth-potential they are, can teach us to progressively uncover our *Whole Self*.

Maturation (aging) is our "master teacher," illuminating our minds and bending our hearts toward the reality that this world is one of tension. Our job is to embrace the totality of it and bring the forces of God together with the seemingly contrary forces of the commercial world, to form some internal unity and integrated wholeness. Our *Whole Self*, then, is not a blemish-free, white-as-snow creation; rather, it is an amalgam of formerly discordant forces, which gradually come together and create an inner balance heretofore unknown. This emergent balance is what we call wisdom!

How to Honor your Whole Self

What are the means we can use to facilitate our journey toward honoring the *Whole Self*? How can we hasten our steps toward God?

1. **Discernment.** Discernment means listening for God's voice speaking to us in those ordinary places and everyday times, and being able to distinguish it from among the many conflicting voices that crowd our lives. Bishop Robert F. Morneau describes discernment in his book <u>Spiritual Direction</u>, *"Discernment is the art of recognizing what God is asking of us – what he would like us to do with our lives, how he wishes us to respond to the concrete life-situations which we encounter following our vocation."*

Discernment allows us to sift through the many voices that continually beckon us, and to distinguish the kernels of truth that free us from the chaff that congests our lives.

How do we do this? Discernment itself is a gift, yet it requires much work on our part to move us to a

217

spiritual disposition that facilitates the germination of the gifts in our soul. We till our "soul-soil" with tools like patience, harmony, faith, and trust. We find ourselves actively stepping out in trust, taking small risks, stretching ourselves beyond our comfort zone, creating tension within. In such ways, we cultivate our garden, making the soil receptive to the seed when it is sown. Our anticipatory care of the garden creates a nourishing seedbed which protects and encourages the seed to grow into a seedling and survive on its own.

Discernment starts from the belief that God is communicating with us all the time.

In this belief, we open ourselves wide to receive God. We "tune in" as it were, to God's wavelength, keeping that line clear, lest it be disconnected or, more likely, overrun by the static of the world. God's call to us is steady yet quiet, omnipresent yet peaceful. We discern God's call in the unfolding of the daily fabric of life: when we believe in quiet; when we see the vision of Jesus reflected just beyond the physical plane; when we think with our noble minds; when we choose in harmony with God's call; and when we act in the confidence of Jesus. All of this is discernment.

2. **Recollection.** A second means of being open to your *Whole Self* is through the process we call recollection. Every day, I forget who I am. I find

myself running around performing a set of roles that, when examined under the microscope of spiritual scrutiny, I find to be far afield from the actual person I am. I so often act as a child of the world. In those situations, I seem to enter a land of forgetfulness, where my actual identity as a child of God is completely absent from my conscious mind, as though it didn't exist.

Such forgetfulness distorts reality and invents fragmented identities of delusion. In the blink of an eye, I can superimpose these delusional identities over the real me and "believe" that the delusion, this manufactured role, is the true "me." If I do this time and again without stopping to recollect my inner truth, I become lost in my delusions. I reduce my *whole self* to a mere collection of roles that represent only the "off-center" parts of me.

Instead of living the "whole" life that I was destined to live, I flounder in my fragments.

I become increasingly vulnerable to invasions from outside, and I find little lasting happiness. I need to remember who I am more often. I need to keep a portion of my internal focus on the candle that burns within me and illumines the truth of whom I am. I need to remain mindful of the truth about me, even as I busy myself in the world.

Recollection means to re-collect to various parts of ourselves and integrate them according to God's music in us. Father Bennet Kelley tells us in his book Spiritual Direction According to St. Paul of the Cross that: *"Paul...did not see recollection as depending on attention of the intellect, but on focusing the heart, or will, on God."* This is comforting to me. I can engage my intellect, the conscious part of my mind, in the task at hand and yet not discount my recollection of God in my heart. I haven't forgotten God but only temporarily put God outside my intellect and into my heart for "safe-keeping." I remain mindful of God's presence within, yet my mindfulness radiates from my heart rather than the rational center of my intellect.

3. **Mystery.** Discovering our *Whole Self* means entering into the profound mystery of life. We live in the paradoxical mystery of how we are in the world and yet not of it; of how we are loved unconditionally while we are sinners; of how we can be strong when we are weak; of how the music of God plays continuously in us yet we may not hear it; and of how God is everywhere yet we don't see God. Still, it is precisely the experience and appreciation of the mystery that can fortify our faith. We generate a mind-set that mystery leads us, that there is a backdrop of activity just beyond the veil of material reality. The world beyond is where we can find our true and whole selves.

We catch glimpses of this world of mystery in our prayer, reflection, quietness, and in our loving relationships with one another. Mystery adds richness to an otherwise sterile existence of serving only worldly tasks. Mystery provides for us another meaning of our daily lives, a meaning that far exceeds anything that the world has to offer. Mystery brings together our disparate parts into a whole that otherwise could not be known.

Recognizing the mystery means dipping into what Carolyn Gratton calls "an alternate consciousness" (in <u>The Art of Spiritual Guidance</u>).

Clues to the mystery of God lie all around us all the time, yet if we find no interest in them, or if we are obtuse in our sensitivity to their presence, we miss the mystery altogether.

Perceiving the mystery requires another way of seeing and evaluating what is actually there. Mystery helps us peer over the ridges of our mental and spiritual ruts and realize that our labels are insufficient, that all our "parts" can work together and bring harmony.

4. **Surrender.** Most of us are of two minds about surrender. On the one hand, we extol surrender as a means of escaping this world of confusion and tasting a bit of the harmony of the next. On the other hand, we live in a culture that abhors submission, passivity, docility, and dependence – all apparent aspects of surrender.

Exactly what is surrender? In his incisive article, "The Role of Surrender in Midlife Spirituality," Martin Helldorfer maintains that *"surrender is neither passive nor an escape; it is an active*

221

engagement of our Whole Self in God's work." Surrender means suspending attachment to our plans, agendas, or outcomes, and turning toward God's plans and outcomes. Surrender does not mean withdrawal from life but active participation in it from the standpoint of God's desires. As we mature, we surrender our desires in deference to the more noble, long-lasting, and real desires God has planned for us.

Surrender moves us toward more authentic living in that it involves our giving up of the inane notion that we can rid ourselves of mistakes, failures, unpleasantries, and self-absorption. Surrender involves exhuming these noxious parts of us to the light of day where they can be examined with caution and care, lest they fester in the underworld of our lives and eventually erupt with damaging effect.

Surrender means living fully, engaging completely, and participating generously in life to the fullest.

Surrender requires that we come in contact with our own desires... for we cannot give over what we aren't aware that we possess.

Surrender requires truthfulness, looking even at the less attractive parts of ourselves and claiming them as our own. Surrender stipulates that we awaken to all of ourselves, and give over our ego desires, our shadows of fear, and our compulsions of control in service to our gifted, spiritual, and *Whole Selves*.

PHANTOM OF THE OPERA

Andrew Lloyd Webber's fantastic musical, *Phantom of the Opera*, is a marvelous story portraying the tension between our true and our false selves. You may recall that the play opens with Christine taking over the star singing role in an opera. She becomes star-struck; she so wants to be the very best singer possible. Her desire for greatness, even in this sweet and seemingly innocent person, is so intense that she will give herself away. On the night of her first performance, she reveals that another force has been guiding her. The force is portrayed in the play as speaking to Christine through a mirror, yet we can question: Is this force outside of Christine or inside her? The force announces himself to Christine as the "angel of music," someone who could teach her to be great.

But is this "angel" real, or is he simply an illusion, something created by Christine? Christine wants desperately to be a great singer; she is willing to do anything, even give away her real self. We are not quite sure when the "angel" is transformed into the Phantom, but gradually his predatory nature begins to unfold. Several meetings between Christine and the Phantom ensue, even one where he demands, "Sing for me!" Christine is tempted to go give up her real self and become one with the Phantom, ready to enter into a nether world, where the forces of darkness triumph over the forces of light.

In the second act – in spite of Raoul, the love of her life, who represents the forces of light and joy, the forces of

223

life – the Phantom succeeds in beckoning Christine into his liar, portrayed as the foggy underworld of the Opera house itself. Once there, with a wedding gown already prepared, and singing the haunting "Past the Point of No Return," the Phantom gives her what looks like an ultimatum: stay with him and marry him; otherwise her lover, who has pursued them there, will die. But, in the final scene, realizing that Christine sees him for what he is, as well as the undying love between Christine and Raoul, the Phantom resigns himself to these facts and lets them go.

These are the desires that created Christine's Phantom; her own inner drives created the horrible tension that almost tore her apart. Only through struggling "to the point of death" with her own compulsive and ego-driven desires to be great in the eyes of humankind, does Christine find freedom from the Phantom.

All of us have our own phantoms, forces of darkness that at times only nip at our heels, while at other times seem so powerful that they can take over our lives.

In some cases this actually happens; some of us can actually forfeit ourselves to the phantoms in our lives. These forces beckon us, as Christine was beckoned by her phantom. They strike at our points of vulnerability and beckon us, each in their own way, away from the forces of truth and goodness. They contort us into performing artificial roles in our lives, rather than living a whole life.

If Andrew Lloyd Webber could continue the play, my hope is that he would have Christine reconcile the disparate forces of darkness and of light that brought so much tension into her life. For we are all called to integrate the forces of light and darkness within us, we are all called to be great. Yet, our ego interprets this as pursuing greatness in our own eyes or the eyes of others. We seek security, approval, and control. Each of these can become so distorted that we can actually forfeit our true selves and take on another role, which bears little resemblance to who we really are. In effect, we figuratively sell our souls to the devil.

RECOLLECTION: A PROCESS OF DEEPER UNDERSTANDING

Recollection means to re-collect the various notes that constitute the core music of ourselves and integrate these notes into symphony according to God's music sheet. I am made of many different parts. At the core of me is goodness, yet surrounding this quiet center orbits a cacophony of sounds, tumbling notes, some strident, some blaring, some only half notes, but all sounds that may not be calling me in the direction that I would choose with my God-conscious mind. Recollection means that I re-collect all these various notes and assemble them into some order, according to the guiding principles and priorities that direct my life.

Recollection is a prayerful means of centering ourselves, of spiritually grounding ourselves, so we can tap into the peace and security that survives in the deepest cervices of our soul.

> *Each day, I need to remind myself at various points during the day that I am who and what I am: a Child of God. I belong to God, not to the world.*

Yet, even my existential flip-flopping between two levels benefits me. It creates tension in my life from which God can further uncover my *Whole Self*.

Recollection is valuable in very practical ways. Recollection can show us that the tension we would like to flush from our lives actually serves us by offering opportunities for our faults to become reconciled with our gifts.

One of the blocks that we often experience on the road to recollection is when we encounter our own "faults." When this happens – as it must since we are a mixture of gifts, shadows, and compulsions – we can stumble over our "faults" and find ourselves stuck right there (See www.healyourillness.com). The essential purpose for recollection, to recall who we really are by centering ourselves on the peace deep within, can be thwarted when we over-focus on our faults.

Father Bennet Kelley says, *"We do not easily come to peace in accepting ourselves especially with our faults."* But he continues, *"Only slowly do we grow in awareness that our faults do not in the least lessen God's love for us."* How wonderful! Here is another gift of maturation: we come to recognize that God loves us unconditionally. Such a realization could not be understood in our youth.

It is only in our maturing years when we enjoy the experience of knowing that we can never strip away our faults or defects – that they are parts of us we must reconcile... we can find the elegant solution to our faults. In our unenlightened youth we may have thought that our faults could eventually be cleansed from us. Such, of course, is not possible.

> *Now that we are blessed with maturity,*
> *we can begin the true integration*
> *process of bringing together in musical*
> *harmony all the disparate sounds that*
> *belong to us.*

Saint Paul of the Cross, founder of the Passionist Order of nuns, brothers, and priests, once encouraged one of his spiritual directees: *"...don't ever let yourself be disturbed by your own faults."* This is good news. When we take such spiritual direction to heart, we come to recognize our faults, give them the due they must have, and catapult right over them. In this way, we refrain from artificially empowering our faults to such a degree that they hobble our faith journey. Our advancing maturity gradually allows the spiritual dawn to illuminate the truth about our faults. They serve a necessary purpose of reminding us that we need to move to our center. Our faults signal us when we are off-center and need to move back. Our faults are very functional for us in this way.

MYSTERY IN THE MEDIA

The media, especially TV and movies, has a long-standing intrigue with mystery. No, I'm not talking about murder mysteries, as in *Mystery Science Theater;* I'm referring to various productions that attempt to portray that we are not alone here, that we have unseen friends all around who know what we are about and who seem to care about us very much.

One very popular TV series was *Touched by an Angel*. Here we saw episodes where three angels took human form and always seemed to find people in various degrees of grim circumstances. The show usually unfolded with one or more of the angels presenting, in angelic quality, the target character of the show (usually the one in the most trouble) with an ethical and behavioral choice. One decision would keep the character in exactly the human dilemma where he or she finds himself, while another decision would somehow extricate this person from the mess.

The movie, *City of Angels,* depicts angels in invisible form. However, there are many, many angels all around. Their main job seems to be escorting persons who have died on their journey beyond the earth. The story unfolds as one angel falls in love with a human. The story ends very sadly.

Both of these shows tell of our fascination with mystery, the fact that God is somehow with us all the time. God is watching us and will never abandon us. Living in the mystery of life means that we see our lives not merely as flesh and bones, as mere material existence; rather, we see our lives as a journey through mystery. We firmly believe that God is present in some form all of our lives, yet we can't explain it or rationally prove it to be true. Who among us has not wondered if some quizzical event was merely coincidence or whether God's hand was somehow involved in it? So much of our lives we cannot explain, so many paradoxes for us to consider; yet as we mature, the paradoxes become more evident and help us explain the real nature of our lives.

Mystery adds magnificently to the richness and the added dimensions of an otherwise sterile existence of serving only the tasks of the world.

Mystery provides for us another meaning of our daily lives, a meaning that far exceeds anything that the world has to offer.   Mystery brings together disparate parts into a whole that otherwise cannot be known. Some of us live out our entire lives without recognizing what is always right in front of us... namely, the realization of the mystery that approaches answering the biggest life question of all: *why?*

Clues and cues of the mystery of God are around us all the time, yet if we find no interest in them, are obtuse in our sensitivity to their presence, or become stuck in the cow paths of our rational mind, we miss the mystery altogether. The mystery requires another way of seeing, another way of evaluating, and another way of feeling what is actually there. When we are stuck in ruts, we miss the grand opportunity of finding integration among the various parts of ourselves. We are stuck in thinking that some of these parts of ourselves are "good" and other parts of ourselves are "bad." Mystery helps us peer over the ridges of our ruts and realize that our labels are insufficient, that all our parts can work together and bring harmony.

THE LIFE OF SURRENDER: MAHATMA GANDHI

Mahatma Gandhi was an unassuming, British-educated lawyer from India who rocked the world. He led the nation of India out of the British Empire to independence. His tool was not violence – no guns, no armies, no armored tanks, no battle casualties. There had been too much of that in the two horrific world wars that had already been waged in the twentieth century, he reasoned. He set out in a very different direction. His most potent "weapon" in the march to free India was surrender. Gandhi's tactic was called non-violence at the time, but the more accurate term to describe his action is surrender. Surrender is a potent tool.

As we mature, we come closer to gaining an understanding of this most intriguing power of surrender. Surrender does not mean submission, passivity, docility, or dependence... quite the contrary. Surrender is an active engagement of our *Whole Self*. In Gandhi's time, he used surrender to lock on to a singular goal – in his case the independence of India. He was able to stifle the forces within himself and the avalanche of forces outside himself who wanted to organize the armies and confront the British army by force. This was not Gandhi's way. He used the weapons of patience, clear thinking, disengagement, noninvolvement, and inner strength to achieve his goal. For Gandhi, it was inaccurate to call the goal of an independent India "his" goal. Gandhi saw the attainment of independence as God's goal. In effect, Gandhi suspended his own goals, he detached from any forcefulness that others would have used, and surrendered his will to God's will.

On a personally spiritual level, surrender means suspending our attachment to our outcomes, our own plans, our own agenda, or our own self-driven projected destiny and instead turning toward God's plans and God's outcomes.

Surrender does not mean withdrawal from life, but active participation in life from the standpoint of God's desires.

As we mature, we successively surrender our own desires in deference to the nobler, more long lasting, and more real desires God has planned for us.

Surrender moves us toward more authentic living in that it involves giving up the inane notions that we can strip ourselves of mistakes, failures, unpleasantries, and self-absorption. Rather, surrender involves unearthing these noxious parts of ourselves to the light of day. Surrender means living fully, engaging completely, and participating generously in life.

INSIGHT QUESTIONS

1. How do you honor your Whole Self?

2. How much of your life is "ego-driven?"

3. What do you see as the connections between your overall well being and your Whole Self?

4. What are your thoughts about "living in tension?"

5. What are your "phantoms?"

References

INTRODUCTION

Senior Adult Ministry. 24 June 2009
<http://www.SeniorAdultMinistry.com>.

Morley, John (editor). Endocrinology of Aging. Totowa, N.J:
Humana Press, 1999.

Siegel, Bernie S. Peace, Love & Healing Bodymind
Communication and the Path to Self-Healing : An
Exploration. New York: Perennial Library, 1990.

Maddi, Salvatore R. Hardy Executive Health Under Stress.
Homewood, Ill: Dow Jones-Irwin, 1984.

Maddi, Salvatore R. and Deborah M. Khoshaba. Resilience
at Work: How to Succeed No Matter What Life Throws at
You. New York: AMACOM/American Management
Association, 2005.

CHAPTER ONE

Arloski, Michael. Wellness Coaching for Lasting Lifestyle
Change. Mahwah: Whole Person Associates, Inc., 2007.

Avila, St. Teresa of. Interior Castle. Garden City: Image,
1972.

Myss, Caroline M. Creation of Health: The Emotional,
Psychological, and Spiritual Responses that Promote
Health and Healing. New York: Three Rivers Press, 1998.

Myss, Caroline M. <u>Entering the Castle: An Inner Path to God and Your Soul</u>. New York: Free Rivers Press, 2007.

Travis, John W., and Regina Sara Ryan. <u>The Wellness Workbook: How to Achieve Enduring Health and Vitality</u>. New York: Celestial Arts, 2004.

CHAPTER TWO

Johnson, Richard P. <u>All My Days: A Personal Life Review</u>. Liguori: Liguori Publications, 2000.

Pieper, Josef. <u>Leisure: The Basis of Culture</u>. Indianapolis: Liberty Fund, 1999.

Edgington, DeGraaf, Dieser, & Edgington. <u>Leisure and Life Satisfaction: Foundational Perspectives</u>. New York: McGraw-Hill, 2006.

CHAPTER THREE

Pinneau, Samuel R. <u>Changes in Intelligence Quotient, Infancy to Maturity: New Insights from the Berkeley Growth Study With Implications for the Stanford-Binet Scales, and Applications to Professional Practice</u>. Boston: Houghton Mifflin, 1961.

Fixx, James F. <u>Jim Fixx's Second Book of Running: The All-New Companion to The Complete</u>. New York: Random House, 1980.

Johnson, Richard P. <u>Discover Your Spiritual Strengths</u>, St. Louis: AGES Press, 2008.

CHAPTER FOUR

Goleman, Daniel. <u>Mind Body Medicine: How to Use Your Mind for Better Health</u>. New York: Consumer Reports Books, 1995.

Johnson, Richard P. <u>Body Mind Spirit: Tapping the Healing Power Within You: A 30-Day Program</u>. Liguori, MO: Liguori Publications, 1992.

CHAPTER FIVE

Whitehead, Evelyn Eaton. <u>Seasons of Strength: New Visions of Adult Christian Maturing</u>. New York: Backinprint.com, 2003.

CHAPTER SIX

Maslow, Abraham H. <u>Farther Reaches of Human Nature</u>. New York, N.Y., U.S.A: Arkana, 1993.

Johnson, Richard P. <u>Loving for a Lifetime 6 Essentials for a Happy, Healthy, and Holy Marriage</u>. Liguori: Liguori Lifespan, 2002.

Johnson, Richard P. <u>Christian's Guide to Mental Wellness How to Balance (Not Choose Between) Psychology and Religion</u>. Liguori, MO: Liguori Publications, 1990.

CHAPTER SEVEN

Alvin, Toffler. <u>Future Shock</u>. New York: Bantam, 1984.

Gladwell, Malcolm. <u>The Tipping Point: How Little Things Can Make a Big Difference</u>. Boston: Back Bay Books, 2002.

Kotter, John P. <u>Leading Change</u>. Boston, Mass: Harvard Business School Press, 1996.

Smith, Douglas K. <u>Taking Charge of Change: 10 Principles for Managing People and Performance</u>. New York: Basic Books, 1997.

CHAPTER EIGHT

Bristol, Claude M., and Harold Sherman. <u>The Power Within You</u>. New York: Fireside, 1992.

Hill, Napoleon, and W. Stone. <u>Success Through a Positive Mental Attitude</u>. New York: Pocket, 2007.

Loehr, James E. <u>The New Toughness Training for Sports: Mental, Emotional, and Physical Conditioning from One of the World's Premier Sports Psychologists</u>. New York: Plume, 1995.

CHAPTER NINE

Johnson, Richard P. <u>Discover Your Spiritual Strengths</u>, St. Louis: AGES Press, 2008.

Johnson, Richard P. <u>All My Days: A Personal Life Review</u>. Liguori, MO: Liguori Publications, 2000.

Rohr, Richard. <u>Everything Belongs: The Gift of Contemplative Prayer</u>. New York: Crossroad Publications, 2003.

Rohr, Richard. <u>Simplicity, Revised and Updated: The Freedom of Letting Go</u>. New York: Crossroad General Interest, 2004.

CHAPTER TEN

Camus, Albert. The Myth of Sisyphus (Penguin Modern Classics). New York: Penguin Books Ltd, 2006.

Frankl, Viktor E. Man's Search for Meaning. New York: Beacon Press, 2006.

Kimble, Melvin. Aging and the Search for Meaning in *Spiritual Maturity in Later Years* (James J. Seeber, editor) Haworth Press, 1990, p. 114.

Sheen, Fulton J. Life is Worth Living (First and Second Series). San Francisco: Ignatius Press, 1999.

Seeber, James. Spiritual Maturity in the Later Years. New York: Haworth Press, 1990.

CHAPTER ELEVEN

Michael, Casey. Sacred Reading: The Ancient Art of Lectio Divina. Liguori, MO: Triumph Books, 1996.

Pennington, M. Basil. A Place Apart: Monastic Prayer and Practice for Everyone. Liguori, MO: Liguori/Triumph, 1998.

Webster's Unabridged Dictionary, Second Edition. New York: Random House, 1997.

Rupp, Joyce. Out of the Ordinary: Prayers, Poems, and Reflections for Every Season. Notre Dame, Indiana: Ave Maria Press, 2000.

Verity, Peter. Out of the Ordinary: Awareness of God in the Everyday. Liguori, MO: Liguori, 1998.

Barrry, William, A. & Connolly, Wiliam, J. The Practice of Spiritual Direction. San Francisco: Harper San Francisco, 1999.

Clemmons, William P. Discovering the Depths. Nashville: Broadman Press, 1976.

Gratton, Carolyn. The Art of Spiritual Direction. New York: Crossroad, 1995.

Kelley, Bennet. Spiritual Direction According to St. Paul of the Cross. Staten Island, N.Y: Alba House, 1993.

Kidd, Sue Monk. When the Heart Waits: Spiritual Direction for Life's Sacred Questions (Plus). New York: Harper San Francisco, 2006.

Helldorfer, Martin. "The Role of Surrender in Midlife Spirituality," Human Development, Volume 16, Number 1. Spring 1995, pages 5-9.

Morneau, Robert F. Spiritual Direction: Principles and Practices. New York: Crossroad, 1996.

Stinissen, Wilfried. The Gift of Spiritual Direction: On Spiritual Guidance and Care for the Soul. Liguori, MO: Liguori Publications, 1999.